NVQ Engineering
Level 2

Electrical Option Units

In memory of Tara

NVQ Engineering
Level 2

Electrical Option Units

Chris Shelton

LONGMAN

Addison Wesley Longman Limited
Edinburgh Gate, Harlow
Essex CM20 2JE, England
and Associated Companies throughout the world

© Addison Wesley Longman Limited 1998

Visit Addison Wesley Longman on the world wide web
at http://www.awl-he.com

First published 1998

British Library Cataloguing-in-Publication Data
A catalogue record for this title is available from the British Library

ISBN 0–582–31561–1

Set by 35 in 10/12 pt Garamond
Produced by Addison Wesley Longman Singapore (Pte) Ltd.,
Printed in Singapore

Contents

3 Basic electronic assembly and wiring   159

Appendices   197

Preface

This book has been mapped to the requirements and standards of **City and Guilds** course **No. 2222 NVQ** in **Engineering Manufacture (Foundation) Level 2 – Electrical Options**. It has been written in a reader-friendly way, providing data and practical advice in a straightforward manner, together with numerous explanatory diagrams. Throughout the work-book there are many numerical/written questions and also practical assignments to be undertaken. These written and practical exercises provide a sound method for learning a new skill as all practical assignments carried out by the student will be verified by an assessor. This verification will then become an important part of the student's portfolio.

The knowledge gained from this book will enable the student to build on basic skills and gain confidence. In order to provide additional help and understanding, this work-book has many illustrative diagrams, photographs and informative tables.

Graphical symbols used throughout this book are generally taken from British Standard 3939, but where additional clarity is required, pictograms are provided and used as an alternative.

Chris Shelton
July 1997

Acknowledgements

I would like to thank the following for their assistance and time given in the preparation of this book.

Special thanks to my wife Shirley, who acted as my literary adviser and translator of technical text into understandable and readable English; Andrea Shelton for her photographic work and patience; and Christopher Barr for illustrating the figures on pp. 83–4.

I would also like to thank the following companies and technical establishments for their help in the making of this work-book: Robin Electronics Ltd, RS Electronics Ltd, and Walsall Conduits Ltd. The author and publishers are grateful for permission to reproduce this copyright material.

Extracts from BS 3939 are reproduced with permission of BSI. Complete copies of BS 3939 can be obtained by post from BSI Customer Services, 389 Chiswick High Road, London W4 4AL; telephone 0181 996 7000.

Finally I would like to thank the staff at Addision Wesley Longman Higher Education for making this book possible.

Chapter 1
Basic electrical measurement

1.21 Precautions taken when using electrical equipment	81		
1.22 First aid procedures	84		
1.23 Using test instruments safely	86		
All information presented in this section is complete, accurate and legible			
All information presented in this section is in the format required			
The trainee observes statutory regulations at all times			
The trainee implements safe operating practice and always demonstrates regard for the safety of others			

Introduction

Part 7 of the **IEE *Wiring Regulations*** describes in detail how an installation should be tested and inspected before commissioning takes place.

It is essential to understand how test instruments are used and to know their limitations. Accordingly the following instruments will be studied:

- Continuity tester
- Ohm meter
- Insulation tester
- Multimeter

Test leads and probes

All test instruments have insulated test leads and probes, which enable values to be taken from the circuit being tested. Test leads are manufactured to the requirements of **GS 38** (General Series 38). Test lead accessories such as **crocodile clips**, **probes** and **fused prods** should be either 'snap-lock' fitted or screw-fitted to the test lead to ensure firm contact.

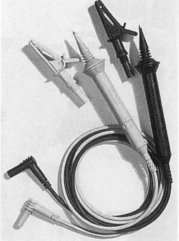

Leads and probes serving a test instrument.
(Reproduced by kind permission of Robin Electronics Ltd.)

Briefly, the GS 38 directive recommends the following:

Test instrument leads must:

- Be adequately insulated.
- Be about 1.2 m in length.
- Not have exposed conductive parts other than the probe tips.
- Be coloured **red** for **live** or positive and **black** for **neutral** or negative.
- Be strong but flexible and with a conductor size of 1.5 mm^2, which has been doubly insulated.
- Be designed so that exposed conductors are not accessible to an operative's fingers if a test lead becomes detached from a probe or from the instrument while values are being taken.
- Be protected by a fuse when used for voltage measurement.

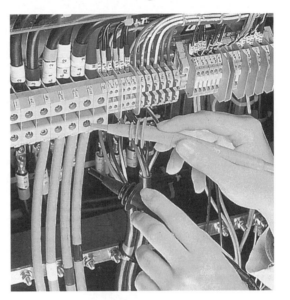

Test leads must be long enough to work with.
(Reproduced by kind permission of Robin Electronics Ltd.)

Test lead probes should:

- Have no more than 2 mm exposed metal tip at the 'working end'.
- Ideally be spring loaded to screen the probe tip when testing a conductive part.
- Ideally have mounded **finger barriers** as illustrated here.

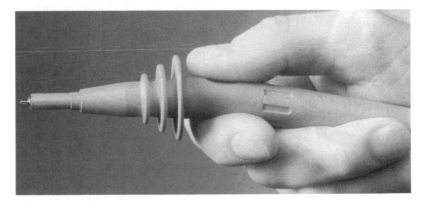

Finger guards are designed to prevent accidental contact with live conductive parts.
(Reproduced by kind permission of Robin Electronics Ltd.)

Health and safety

The cause of accidents when using test instruments

There are many varied reasons for accidents with test instruments. Often they occur due to carelessness, lack of training or inexperience. Other reasons are:

- Unsuitable test leads
- Cracked or broken probes
- Probe tip too long, causing a short circuit condition
- Too much current is drawn through the instrument
- Instrument is set to the wrong function
- Arc flash-overs causing burns to fingers

Precautions

Engineers can avoid potential dangers when using test instruments by keeping to the following safety rules:

- Never take risks with electricity.
- Keep to the recommended procedures.
- Avoid using old-fashioned leads, probes and meters.
- If unsure of the expected values, work down from the highest range to a sensible working range.
- Check for defects (broken or cracked cases, damaged leads or probes, loose terminals and connections).
- Correct defects as soon as possible.

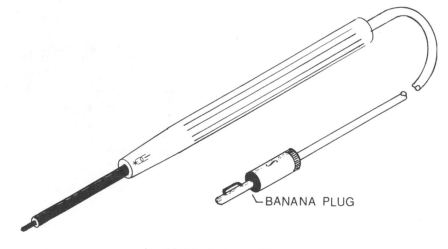

An old style instrument test lead.

Display scales

Test instruments have one of the following three types of display panels:

1. Digital
2. Digital with bar graph **analogue indicator**
3. Analogue

Digital display panel serving a continuity meter. (Reproduced by kind permission of Robin Electronics Ltd.)

Digital display with bar graph indicator. (Reproduced by kind permission of Robin Electronics Ltd.)

Analogue display serving a hand cranked insulation tester. (Reproduced by kind permission of Robin Electronics Ltd.)

Middle-priced multimeters have facilities to measure the following:

- AC and DC voltages (volts)
- AC and DC current (amps)
- Electrical resistance (ohms)
- Electrical continuity (ohms)

Continuity tester

This type of instrument is used to measure the precise resistance of a conductor. The measurement shows whether the wire has breaks or loose connections that could cause electrical problems when on load.

For example, to check that a current-carrying conductor serving a workshop machine has no faults, the following steps should be taken. Before starting, remember to make sure that the meter has a healthy battery.

1. Isolate the electrical supply serving the machine.
2. Disconnect the suspect **load conductor** from the machine isolator.
3. Open the terminal box serving the machine.
4. Disconnect the supply conductor.
5. Set the instrument to the **continuity range**.
6. Touch the test instrument leads together to produce **0000** on a digital meter or **zero** ohms on an analogue instrument.
7. Connect the test leads to each end of the suspected conductor and press the test button. A conductor without faults will produce a very low value of less than 1 ohm, but if the wire is broken or loose within a terminal housing a much higher reading can be expected. If the conductor has a clean break an infinitive reading will be displayed.

Some continuity testers are equipped with internal buzzers. This helps when continuity has to be measured instead of the actual resistance of a conductor.

Values displayed are in **ohms**. An ohm is defined as:

The ratio of the potential difference (in volts) across an electrical component to the current (in amps) passing through it. Resistance is measured in ohms and is a measure of opposition to the flow of electricity.

Ohm's Law

In 1827, **Georg Simon Ohm** discovered that the resistance of a conductor of electricity was directly proportional to its length and inversely proportional to its cross-sectional area, providing the temperature of the material was constant

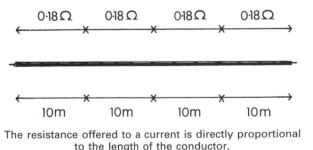

The resistance offered to a current is directly proportional to the length of the conductor.

The electrical resistance of a material is measured in **ohms** (symbol Ω), and in most materials a rise in temperature will create a proportional rise in resistance.

Ohm's Law states that:

The current flowing in a circuit is directly proportional to the voltage applied and inversely proportional to the resistance at a constant temperature.

Mathematically this law may be expressed as:

$$I = \frac{V}{R}$$

where I is the value of the current in **amps**
           V is the applied voltage in **volts**
           R is the total resistance in **ohms**

As an example, study the following problem.
Problem:
A wire-wound resistor of unknown value has been added to complete a simple circuit. By measurement the applied voltage was found to be 10 volts and the current flow 0.5 amps. Calculate the value of the resistor.
Solution:
By applying Ohms Law,

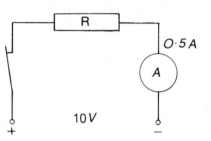

A resistor of unknown value forms a simple circuit drawing
a current of 0.5 amp and is supplied with a power source of 10 volts.

$$I = \frac{V}{R}$$

By cross-multiplying the expression,

$$V = I \times R$$

and dividing the expression throughout by I

$$R = \frac{V}{I}$$

Substituting for known values,

$$R = \frac{10}{0.5}$$

The value of the unknown resistor, $R = 20$ ohms.

Variations in Ohm's Law

The basic form of Ohm's Law was introduced in 1827 but, as shown in the table below, there are many variations of this expression. Ohm's Law is not satisfactory if a calculation has to be made to find the value of **voltage** when the only available data is the power in **watts** generated and the resistance of the circuit in **ohms**.

Current in amps (symbol *I*)	$\frac{V}{R}$	or	$\frac{W}{V}$	or	$\sqrt{\frac{W}{R}}$
Power in watts (symbol *W*)	$V \times I$	or	$I^2 \times R$	or	$\frac{V^2}{R}$
Voltage in volts (symbols can be *E, U* or *V*)	$\sqrt{W \times R}$	or	$I \times R$	or	$\frac{W}{I}$
Resistance in ohms (symbol Ω)	$\frac{V}{I}$	or	$\frac{W}{I^2}$	or	$\frac{V^2}{W}$

Calculating resistance

Let: I equal the current flowing in a circuit
R equal the resistance in ohms of the circuit
V equal the voltage applied to the circuit

Using Ohm's Law,

$$I = \frac{V}{R} \text{ (sometimes written as } I = \frac{E}{R} \text{ or } \frac{U}{R} \text{)}$$

Cross-multiplying the equation above:

$$I \times R = V$$

Dividing each side of the equation by I:

$$R = \frac{V}{I}$$

Let us suppose that a workshop appliance served with 230 volts, AC, is drawing 2.3 amps from a supply. Referring to the last equation above, the total resistance of the circuit in ohms would be:

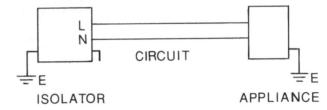

A workshop appliance, served with 230 volts AC is drawing 2.3 amps from the supply.

$$R = \frac{230}{2.3}$$

$$R = 100 \text{ ohms}$$

Resistance must never be measured with a test instrument on a live circuit as the meter will be damaged.

Exercise 1.1

Test instruments and Ohm's Law

1. Without referring to Ohm's Law, briefly describe electrical resistance in practical terms.

2. What basic check should be made before starting a continuity test?

3. Using instrumentation, a 230 volt bench heater is found to be drawing 8.695 amps from the supply. Calculate the resistance in ohms of the element.

Ohm meter

Stand-alone ohm meters are rarely used on site and are normally kept for use in electronic workshops, laboratories and classrooms. A **multimeter** switched to the **ohms** range is the wisest choice for factory use. This type of meter is often supplied with a heavy-duty rubberised holster, which makes the instrument dust-, splash- and knock-proof.

A digital multimeter, supplied with a heavy-duty
rubberised holster, being used as an ohm meter.
(Reproduced by kind permission of Robin Electronics Ltd.)

Types

- Stand-alone   (scaled in ohms)
- Multimeter   (scaled in ohms when reading resistance)
- Milliohm meter   (scaled in one-thousandth part of one ohm)
- Micro-ohmmeter   (scaled in one-millionth part of one ohm)

Application: milli- or micro-ohm meter
The milliohm or micro-ohm meter is an ideal tool for testing the precise electrical conductivity of a welded joint. The lower the value between the sides of the joint the better the electrical conductivity.

Voltage delivered and checks to make
The voltage serving an ohm meter is very small and lies between 3 and 12 volts DC. Always check the instrument for faults or damage before testing is carried out.
A **healthy battery** and **zeroing** test should be made before work commences so that accurate values can be recorded.

Testing procedure

A component such as a **resistor** may be evaluated with a standard multimeter, as shown here. It is important not to handle the component with both hands whilst taking values, because, although the voltage is low, the instrument could record body resistance. This would make the true value of the component impossible to record.

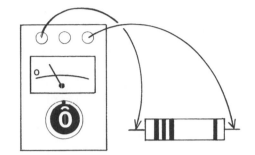

Measuring the resistance of a common resistor.

To test:

1. Check the health of the battery serving the instrument and carry out a zeroing test by placing the leads together.
2. Keep the component away from any source of electrical energy.
3. Check that the instrument has been switched to the **ohms range**.
4. Select the highest ohmic range.
5. Place the instruments leads on either side of the resistor.
6. Select lower ranges if necessary.
7. Read the value of the component in ohms.

Exercise 1.2

Measuring electrical resistance of a welded joint

1. How would you check to ensure perfect electrical continuity of a welded joint?

2. When measuring the resistance of a component, why is it unwise to touch either side of the component with bare hands?

3. For this exercise you will be given a low-value resistor, the value of which will fall between 10 and 50 ohms.

   (a) Demonstrate to your assessor that you are able to carry out formal instrumentation checks before work commences.

   (b) Measure the value of the resistor given to you and record it in the space provided below.

   The value of the resistor is:

   The type of meter used was:

   The make and model number of the instrument:

4. For this exercise you will be given two small sections of metal, which have been joined by means of **welding**.

   (a) Demonstrate to your assessor that you are able to choose the correct instrument for measuring the resistance across the welded joint.

   (b) Show that you can carry out battery-health and instrument-zeroing checks before any values are taken.

   (c) Measure the electrical resistance of the joint in three different places. These are to be known as 'Test A', 'Test B' and 'Test C'.

   (d) Record details in the spaces provided for you below.

   Type of instrument used:

   Resistance value of **Test A**:

   Resistance value of **Test B**:

   Resistance value of **Test C**:

   Make and model number of the instrument:

Insulation tester

Types

- Analogue (electronic)
- Digital (electronic)
- Hand-cranked (electro-mechanical)

Uses

Insulation testers have two types of use:

1. As a continuity meter.
2. As a cable insulation tester.

When the instrument is used as a continuity tester the voltage delivered is small compared with between 240 and 1000 volts when used to measure insulation values. On standard meters there are usually three insulation test voltage ranges:

- 240 volts
- 500 volts
- 1000 volts

On the **continuity scale** all values are read as *ohms*, whereas when switched to the higher voltage insulation test ranges the values displayed are in **megohms**. One megohm is equal to **one million ohms**. When using a digital meter for insulation testing, values will appear on the screen as a decimal part of one million. Two hundred and fifty thousand ohms will appear as 0.25 megohms whereas half a million ohms will be read as 0.5 megohms. However, when insulation values are high, readings may be taken directly from the screen, for example 1.02 megohms, 200 megohms.

A typical insulation tester, ideal for site, workshop or factory use, is shown here. The accuracy factor of an analogue meter is ±1.5% of its total scale. This factor is slightly better when using a digital instrument.

A typical insulation tester. (Reproduced by kind permission of Robin Electronics Ltd.)

Testing procedures

Before testing is carried out, remove or disconnect all current-using equipment from the circuit (examples are lamps, heaters, audio and television receivers, etc.). All electronic devices should be removed from the circuit under test to avoid permanent damage caused by the high voltage test. Switch to the 500 volt scale.

With all switches closed and fuses and circuit breakers in or switched 'ON' the total resistance recorded must not fall below **0.5 megohms** (500 000 ohms) when the nominal voltage of the supply is up to and including 500 volts. Above 500 volts and up to 1000 volts, the minimum insulation resistance between conductors and between conductors and earth should not fall below 1 megohm (1 000 000 ohms). *Wiring Regulation 713-04-04* refers to this.

Obtaining the value of resistance

Be guided by these following points:

1. Ensure that the electrical supply is isolated from the circuit under test and that all electronic devices and appliances have been removed or disconnected.
2. Check the instrument for 'battery-level', if possible, and ensure it is working correctly. This may be done by switching the insulation tester to the 500 volt scale, and touching the leads together while pressing the test button to produce a **'zero'** reading in the display panel. Disconnecting the test leads will produce an **'infinitive'** value in the display panel whilst the test button is pressed.
3. Measure the insulation resistance between all current carrying conductors. How this is carried out when testing a typical three phase, neutral and earth installation is shown here.

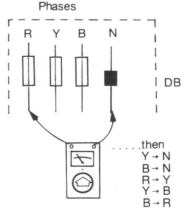

The insulation resistance is measured between all current carrying conductors.

4. Test the insulation resistance existing between each current carrying conductor and the main protective conductor (earth). This should not be less than the values specified.

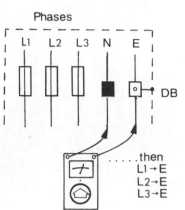

The insulation resistance is measured between all current carrying conductors and the main protective conductor.

5. Finally, check to ensure the total resistance between **all** conductors grouped and bonded together and the **main protective conductor** is not less than the value specified.

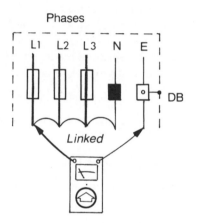

Measure the collective resistance of all current carrying conductors and the main protective conductor.

Values lower than acceptable

Check the circuit to find the reason for any fault condition. This can be carried out using a process of systematic elimination. When the cause has been found, remedial measures should be taken to increase the level of insulation resistance to an acceptable level.

Pinched and scuffed cables or damp plaster and building rubble touching live conductive parts can often cause fault conditions.

Other reasons include the following:

- Squashed cabling
- Vandalism
- Incorrectly connected protective conductor
- Carelessly abandoned cables
- Nails accidentally driven through a conductor to earth
- Accessory boxes carelessly plastered over and left
- Accessory fixing screws driven through a conductor causing a fault problem between **live/neutral** and **earth**
- Green/yellow oversleeving absent from the bare protective conductor causing a fault condition between any live conductor and earth
- Loose and badly connected conductors

Hand-cranked instruments

As the name suggests, power is generated by cranking the handle of an instrument to produce a test voltage. There are no batteries. The instrument is electro-mechanical and can also be used as a continuity tester. The accuracy factor is approximately ±1.5% of the full scale.

Instruments and the *Wiring Regulations*

Part 7 of the *Wiring Regulations* provides information for the inspection and testing of electrical installations.

Good performance standards are required from electrical test instruments and it is recommended they should be professionally *calibrated* once a year, or more frequently if used every day.

Wiring Regulation test instruments include the following:

- Earth loop impedance tester
- Earth electrode/resistance tester
- High-voltage insulation tester – for high-voltage cables (voltages provided are from 2500 to 10 000 volt DC)
- Insulation/continuity tester
- Multimeter
- Residual Current Device timing tester (RCD)

| Exercise 1.3 | *Instruments and insulation testing* |

1. Indicate below whether the following statement is true or false:
Insulation test values must be taken between **all** current carrying conductors serving a triple phase and neutral electrical supply.

True/False

2. For this exercise you will be shown three types of instrument, all of which have been reviewed so far. Each instrument will be reference labelled.

(a) Demonstrate to your assessor that you are able to recognise these instruments and check their accuracy. Calibrate by use of the **adjustment screw** if necessary.
(b) Test meters that are found to be faulty, inaccurate and incapable of calibration must be recorded and reported to an appropriate person.

Instrument reference	Type of instrument, make and model no.	Where best used (factory, site or classroom)	Accuracy report
A			
B			
C			

3. For this practical exercise you will be shown a simulated 400 volt three-phase and neutral installation/circuit, typical of many found in industry.
Alternatively this exercise may be carried out under supervision within the workplace.

(a) Demonstrate to your assessor that you are able to use an insulation test instrument to record the value of this installation/circuit.
(b) Record your findings in the spaces provided.

(c) Insulation values lower than acceptable must be investigated, the cause of the problem identified and put right.

Type of exercise (simulated/workplace):

Type of installation/circuit:

Test voltage applied to the installation/circuit:

Test values obtained*:

- Between L1 and L2:

- Between L1 and L3:

- Between L2 and L3:

- Between L1 and neutral:

- Between L2 and neutral:

- Between L3 and neutral:

- Between neutral and earth:

- Between L1 and earth:

- Between L2 and earth:

- Between L3 and earth:

  * The letter 'L' represents the word 'live' or phase.

Test result comments:

Are the values obtained at an acceptable level?   Yes/No

A multipurpose test instrument. (Reproduced by kind permission of Robin Electronics Ltd.)

Multimeters

A multimeter test instrument can be either an analogue or a digital type and has many test purposes. These include testing of:

- AC and DC voltage (up to 999 volts)
- AC and DC current (up to 400 milliamps and 20 amps)
- Resistance (up to 5000 ohms)
- Batteries
- Frequency (20–200 kilohertz)
- Capacitance (2000 picofarad to 200 microfarad)

Not all multimeters are equipped with such a range of test functions. The accuracy factor for this type of instrument lies between 0.3 and 1.8% of the recorded value and depends upon the make and design of the instrument.

Digital meters

Advantages

- Clear and easy-to-read display
- Automatic scale range (volts and amps)
- Automatic data holding facilities with some models
- Analogue bar graph facilities with some models
- Can display values as low as 0.01 ohm
- Often with audible continuity test facilities

Disadvantages

- Can mistake the position of the decimal point
- Will fluctuate from one value to another when values are low

Analogue meters

Advantages

- Easy to read
- Accurate recording
- Built-in battery-check monitor on many models
- Continuous operation facilities (will not auto cut-out)
- The value indicator does not wobble
- Some models have automatic range-change facilities
- Reading errors are unlikely
- Scale illumination facilities for poor lighting conditions
- Often has anti-parallex mirror facilities
- Live circuit visual indicator
- Zero ohms adjustment for removing the internal resistance of the test leads

Disadvantages

- Can be read from the wrong scale
- Not good for failing eyesight
- Reading the value is slower than from a digital display
- Mistakes can be made when selecting a working scale
- The scale is not uniformed and can become cramped

Evaluating resistance, current and voltage

Before beginning a test, the following steps should be carried out:

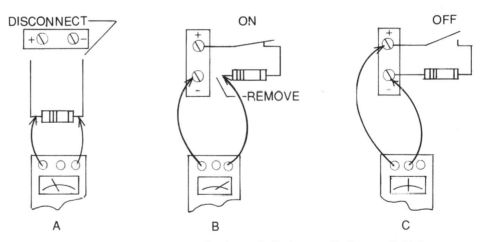

Measuring resistance, current and voltage. A, Resistance; B, Current; C, Voltage.

1. Visually check both instrument leads and probes for damage or defects.
2. Check the battery monitor before measuring resistance and '**zero**' the instrument by placing the tips of the test leads together when switched to the resistance range. Adjust the value indicator pointer with a small screwdriver placed in the **adjustment screw**. This is usually found sited in the centre of the instrument.
3. Select the correct function (resistance, current or voltage) and start at the high end of the scale if you are unsure of the expected value.

| Exercise 1.4 | *Multimeters* |

1. Using your own words state four reasons, in order of merit, why you would choose an analogue multimeter to work with.

2. For this practical exercise you will need the following:

- A multimeter and test leads
- A switched 12 volt 'isolated' supply of electricity
- A work-board
- 300 mm of insulated wire (0.25 or 0.5 mm^2)
- One standard screw-type terminal block rated at 5 amps
- Small fixing screws for the terminal block
- One 12 watt, 22 ohm resistor (for example, silicone-coated wire wound with 30 mm long leads)

Arrange the components in a similar fashion to that shown on p. 15. Cut the block connectors to suit circuit requirements and fix them to the work-board using the small screws provided. Use the connectors to terminate the insulated wire and resistor.

(a) Correctly select the instrument and check for accuracy and damage.

(b) Demonstrate to your assessor that you are able to measure the following values:

- The exact resistance of the resistor selected
- The current flowing through the resistor
- The exact voltage of the source of electricity supplied

(c) Write your answers in the spaces provided.

The total resistance recorded:	ohms
The total current recorded:	amps
The exact voltage of the source of supply:	volts

Instruments: dangers and safety

Engineers working with live conductive parts can be at risk from many potentially dangerous situations. The following list gives some of the most common accidents that occur when test equipment is used.

- Shock
- Arc burns
- Flash-over situations
- Chemical burns when work is carried out on batteries
- Instrument damage caused by the function switch set to the wrong setting
- Accidents caused by untrained or inexperienced operatives
- Damp or wet conditions causing shock or flash-overs
- Inadequately insulated test leads causing shock
- Excessive current causing damage to the instrument

Safety guide-lines

To remove the risk of work-place accidents, the **Health and Safety Exective** (HSE) have issued guide-lines for manufacturers and the users of test instruments. The document containing these guide-lines is the HSE **General Series Directive GS 38** (November 1986), which can be obtained as a photocopy at most leading public libraries.

Briefly, the GS 38 safety requirements are as follows:

1. Instruments should have fused probe leads.
2. Test probes should have finger barriers.
3. The exposed metal probe tip should be no longer than 2 mm and should incorporate a spring-loaded sliding safety shutter.
4. Instruments and test leads/probes should have adequate insulation.
5. Instruments should have suitable test leads and probes.
6. Test leads should be coloured; one red and one black.
7. Test leads should be flexible and strong.
8. Test leads should not have exposed conductors other than at the tips.
9. Each test lead should be approximately 1.2 metres long.
10. Test instruments should be made in a way that does not allow live conductive parts to become accessible to an operative's fingers if a probe becomes detached from a lead.
11. Instruments should be designed with recessed safety terminal ports.

The following necessary precautions should be taken in addition to those above whenever work is carried out using measuring instruments:

- The correct scale must be selected.
- Provide a firm sound connection when testing.
- Aim the test probes to avoid flash-over situations.
- Use instrument probes to GS 38 specifications.
- Check that the instrument is working as intended.
- Inspect the instrument for mechanical damage.
- Keep away from wet situations.
- Be sure that one of the test leads/probes is fitted with a 500 milliamp fuse.
- Choose the highest scale and work down if unsure of the expected value.
- Keep fingers away from live conductive parts – whatever the voltage.

Process for checking tools and equipment before use

It is important to check tools and test instruments before use whenever electrical work is undertaken. Always use insulated tools for the purpose for which they are designed.

Before starting any work, check tools for defects and replace them if necessary. Make sure test instruments function correctly and check the insulation, casing and terminal ports of probes/leads. Report any damage to the supervisor or section leader. Damages should be logged against the serial number/model of the instrument in question.

Disconnection procedure

Accidents involving direct contact with live conductive parts can be minimised by making a routine inspection of the circuit before starting any work. For example, this procedure is particularly important when factory machinery is to undergo a maintenance programme. Such an inspection can be undertaken by following a simple flow-chart.

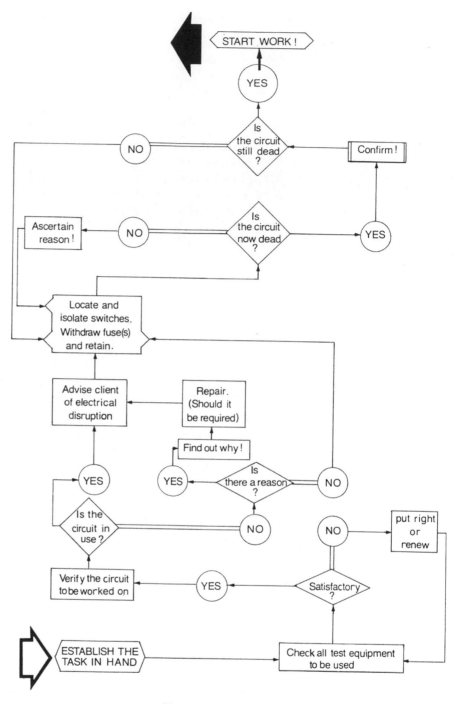

Disconnection procedure.

Exercise 1.5   *Disconnection procedures*

1. Name three types of accident that could arise when using test instruments.

2. State briefly what should always be done before starting a disconnection procedure.

3. A certain amount of role play will be required for this practical exercise. You will be shown a simulated installation where the supply voltage from the distribution centre is no more than 24 volts. Select a suitable instrument for this exercise.

   Please assume the following:

   - A small repair is required on a power circuit serving a workshop/factory machine.
   - Your client will be the machine operator.
   - The circuit is in constant use at all times.
   - The machine is provided with a local isolation switch.

   (a) Using the flow-chart on p. 18 as a guide, demonstrate to your assessor by use of role play and a suitable instrument how a typical disconnection procedure is carried out.
   (b) Talk your way through this exercise.

Conducting and insulating materials

A material, such as copper or gold, which allows electricity to pass through it freely is known as a **conductor**. Materials such as plastic or glass, which resist the passage of electricity, are called **insulators**. A selection of conducting and insulating materials found in electrical engineering is listed in the tables below.

Conductors in order of decreasing electrical conductivity	Element's symbol	Practical use
Gold	Au	Electrical contacts
Silver	Ag	Electrical contacts
Copper	Cu	Switching contacts and cable
Aluminium	Al	Cable and heat sinks, etc.
Mercury	Hg	Switching and AC to DC rectification
Lead	Pb	Cable sheath and special fuse wire; used in electrical solder
Carbon	C	Resistors and 'brushes' for electric motors
Germanium	Ge	Semi-conductors
Tin	Sn	Used in electrical solder

Insulators used in general electrical engineering	Practical use
Ethylene propylene rubber, polythene, natural rubber, polyvinyl chloride (PVC)	Conductor and cable insulation
Bakelite®, Perspex®	Supplementary insulation (electrical cabinets and enclosures)
Ceramics, paper, glass	Capacitors, special insulators, etc.
Oil	High-voltage transformers

Connecting test instruments into a circuit

It is important to connect instruments correctly so that damage is avoided. Ten commonly used test instruments and examples of their use in electrical engineering are given in the table below.

Instrument	Method of testing	Comments	
Ammeter	Connect in series formation with the circuit. Measured in **amperes**.	Disconnect the circuit at a convenient place. Ensure that all connections are sound.	
Voltmeter	Voltage measured in parallel with the circuit. Measured in **volts**.	Place the instrument probes across the incoming live and neutral supply.	
Continuity tester	Test probes are placed at either end of the conductor under test. Measured in **ohms** or **milliohms**.	Isolate the electrical supply and one end of the conductor under test.	
Insulation tester	Test in parallel with the circuit or with any conductor(s) and earth. Measured in **megohms** (10^6 ohms).	Isolate the electrical supply and main **neutral** when testing from a fuseboard. Remove the load from the circuit.	
Kilowatt-hour meter	The windings in the meter are placed in series with the **live** and **neutral** supply conductors. Measured in **units** (1 unit = 1000 **watts** × 1 **hour**)	Place securely in the correct terminals. Values are read directly from the display panel or dials.	
Ohm meter	The instrument test leads are placed in parallel with the component. Measured in **ohms** and **milliohms**.	Clean the leads of the component and place the test leads firmly on each end as shown.	
Watt meter	The instrument should be connected in circuit as illustrated. Measured in **watts** or **megawatts** (10^6 watts).	Break the circuit at convenient points and ensure that all connections are secure.	

Electrical components

There are many electrical components used in everyday electrical engineering. See the table below for some of the more familiar types used in industry.

Component	Function	
Transformer	A device that increases or decreases the value of voltage. It may also be used as a means of isolating power from the main public supply as shown in the bottom illustration, where P = primary winding and S = secondary winding. The top illustration shows a typical door bell transformer.	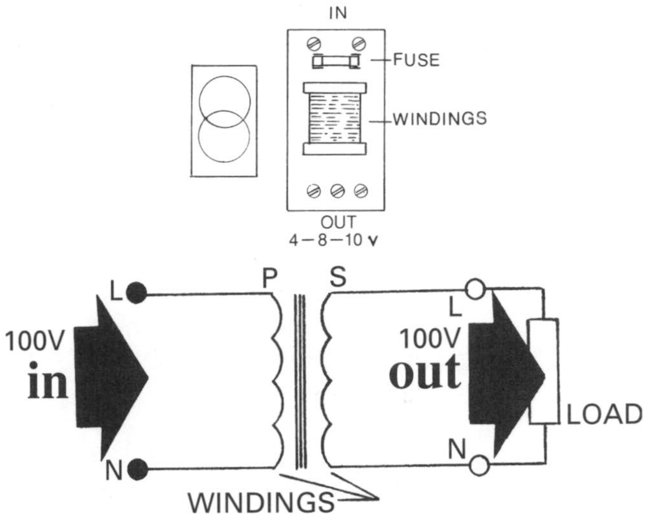
Fuse	Protects a circuit or device from an **overcurrent** condition. Made from a metal alloy of low melting point. Often enclosed in a glass or ceramic cartridge with brass caps as illustrated.	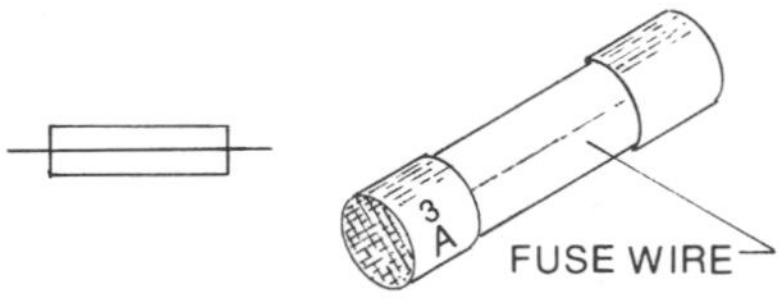
Resistor	A component that is placed in a circuit because of its electrical resistance. May be wire wound or carbon based. Some may be varied by means of an integral sliding or rotary contact.	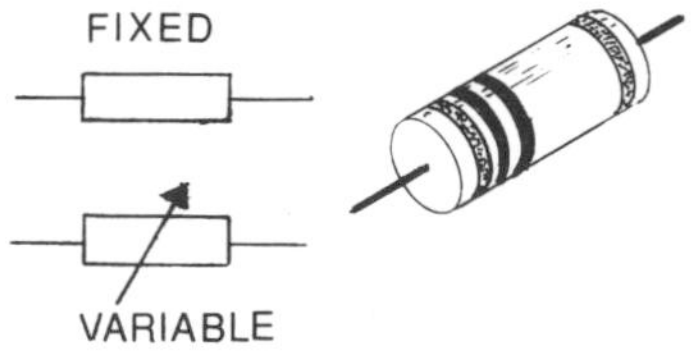
Primary cell (battery)	A means to provide portable DC current based on the dry version of the **Leclanché primary cell**. Each cell has an output of approximately 1.5 volts. Six placed in series formation will provide **9 volts** of electricity.	
Capacitor	A device that has a minimum of two plates separated by a special insulator called a **dielectric**. Capacitors are able to store a charge of electricity and a capacitor is shown here in its simplest form. Capacitance is measured in farads (F).	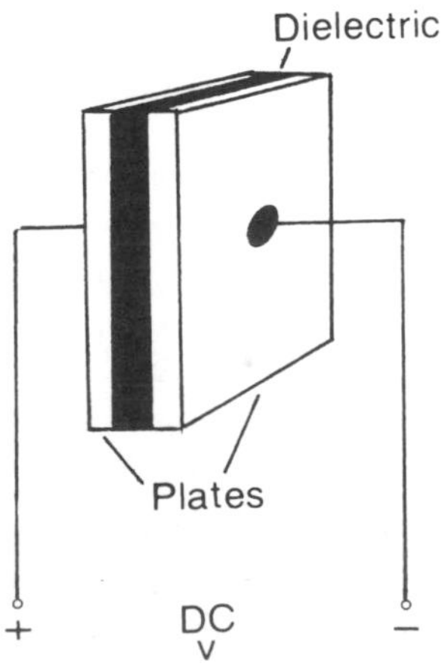

Component	Function	
Lamps and bulbs	Devices that are able to produce a source of artificial light by means of heating an element to white heat. Used for illumination, decoration and as indicator lights, etc.	Glass / Coiled filament / Supplementary supports / Gases (Ar & N) / Glass pillar / Supply leads / Base
Diode	A device that permits the flow of electricity in one direction only. Used in electronics and AC to DC rectifier units.	A B C — A, STANDARD; B, ZENER; C, LIGHT EMITTING
Transistor	A semi-conductor device used in electrical and electronic engineering which is able to amplify and rectify. Often found in control circuits. Symbols: b = base, c = collector and e = emitter.	c b e / e c b
Rectifier	Diodes placed as illustrated converts alternating current into direct current.	dc − N + ~ac L a DC out L b AC in
Thermister	A component that will rapidly decrease in resistance in proportion to temperature. Used to compensate for temperature variations or as a thermometer.	−t° NEGATIVE TEMPERATURE COEFFICIENT

Resistor colour coding

Resistors are coded with **coloured bands** around the body of the resistor to enable their values to be read. Regrettably, resistors are not made to reflect their true value so a **tolerance factor** has to be considered. The tolerance factor is calculated as a plus/minus percentage (±%) of the declared value.

The colour code is designed to be read from left to right with the majority of bands ranged to the left. Each of the coloured bands represents a number, so the value of the component can be determined.

- **Band 1** represents the first number.
- **Band 2** represents the second number.
- **Band 3** represents the **multiplier**.
- **Band 4** (far right) represents the percentage ± tolerance of the resistor.

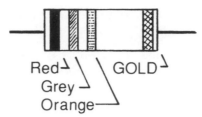

A colour-coded resistor with four bands.

When a resistor has **five** coloured bands, the first three represent the first three numbers. The fourth band then becomes the multiplier and the fifth is the percentage tolerance guaranteed by the manufacturers.

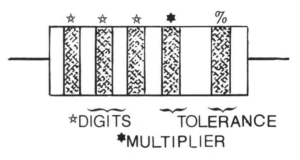

A five-band colour-coded resistor.

The table below provides data to calculate unknown resistor values. For example, a four-band resistor with **brown**, **yellow**, **orange** and **silver** bands will have a nominal value of 14 000 ohms at a ±10% tolerance level. This means that the resistor's value lies somewhere between 12 600 and 15 400 ohms.

Colour of bands 1 to 3 Colour of bands 1 to 4 (BS 1852)	Number	Multiplier (band 3)	Tolerance of resistor as a percentage (band 4)
Black	0	1	–
Brown	1	10	1
Red	2	100	2
Orange	3	1000	–
Yellow	4	10 000	–
Green	5	100 000	–
Blue	6	1 000 000	–
Violet	7	–	–
Grey	8	–	–
White	9	–	–
Gold (last band)	–	–	5
Silver (last band)	–	–	10
No colour (last band)	–	–	20

Remembering the colour code

To recall the colour sequence used to evaluate the numerical value of a resistor, remember the following:

> *Bleached Bread Rarely Offends Young Greedy*
> *Bluebottles Vandalising Grey Wheatmeal.*

The capital letters represent the first letter of the colour serving the colour code in numerical order. For **Bl**eached read Black (0), and for **Br**ead read Brown (1) and so on.

Alphanumerically coded resistors

These are resistors coded with both letters and numbers as shown here. Each value is printed on the body of the resistor together with one or two letters of the alphabet. The first letter indicates the **multiplier** taken from the table below, while the second letter identifies the **tolerance** of the resistor.

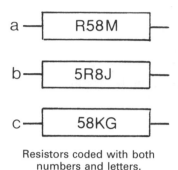

a — R58M —

b — 5R8J —

c — 58KG —

Resistors coded with both numbers and letters.

First letter and multiplier		Second letter and tolerance level as a percentage
R	(× 1)	F (1%)
K	(kilo) (× 10³ or 1000)	G (2%)
M	(mega) (× 10⁶ or 1 000 000)	J (5%)
G	(giga) (× 10⁹ or 1 000 000 000)	K (10%)
T	(tera) (× 10¹² or 1 000 000 000 000)	M (20%)

Resistors with the letter R printed on them also show the position of the decimal point. For example R58M translates to 0.58 ohms at 20% tolerance. When the letter R is placed between two numbers, e.g. 5R8J, the coded value translates to 5.8 ohms at 5% tolerance.

Capacitors

A **capacitor** is an electronic device that will enable an electric charge to be stored when both plates are at **opposite potentials** (that is, one is positively charged, the other is negatively charged).

A few of the many types of capacitors are: **solid tantalum**, **computer grade high ripple**, **polyester**, **high capacity paper** and **ceramic**.

The table below describes four different types of capacitor commonly used in everyday electronics.

Type	Description and use
Fixed non-polarised capacitor	Housed in plastic or metal cans. Have various shapes and sizes. Values from 2.2 picofarads (pF) to many micro-farads (µF). For general use in electronics or in electric motor circuits. 5µF±10% 400v A paper insulated capacitor. A = plates; B = dielectric; C = leads; D = container.
Polarised capacitor	A polarised capacitor has to be connected correctly to the source of the supply. Often housed in single or double ended cans. Sub-miniature polarised capacitors are about 7 × 4 mm in size. Used in radio and television circuitry, etc. 100µF 7mm★ 16mm★ ★APPROX.

Type	Description and use
Trimmer capacitor	Used when final adjustment to a circuit is needed. Usually equipped with a **mica dielectric** and a ceramic base. Adjustment is made by a screwdriver. Typical capacitance swing is from 23 to 22 pF. Various sizes. 40 pF W.21 D.10 H.6 500 pF W.24 D.16 H.5 Mica dielectric and ceramic base. Screwdriver adjustment. Reproduced by kind permission of RS Components Ltd.
Variable air type capacitor	This type of capacitor consists of two metal plates. One plate can be rotated by a central spindle to interleave with the second plate, which is fixed. Both plates are insulated from each other. Used as a tuner in radio sets.

Units of capacitance

1 picofarad (pF) $= 10^{-12}$ farad
1 nanofarad (nF) $= 10^{-9}$ farad
1 microfarad (μF) $= 10^{-6}$ farad
1000 pF $= 1$ nF
1000 nF $= 1$ μF

Capacitor coding

Capacitor coding can vary slightly depending on the origin of manufacture but usually attempts are made to follow the same colour system as laid down for resistors. Large industrial cylindrical-type capacitors have their values printed on the side of their protective containers, whereas smaller types are colour coded as shown here. The value obtained is in picofarads.

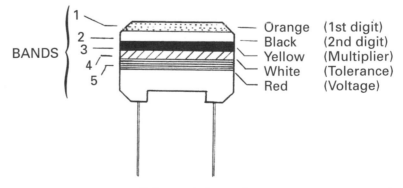

BANDS
1 — Orange (1st digit)
2 — Black (2nd digit)
3 — Yellow (Multiplier)
4 — White (Tolerance)
5 — Red (Voltage)

Colour-coded capacitors.

The capacitor tolerance colour code is slightly different from resistors, as shown in the following table. When reading colour coded capacitors always take the first band of colour to be the one which is furthest from the point of connection.

Colour code	Percentage tolerance (±)
Brown	1
Red	2
Orange	2.5
Green	5
White	10
Black	20

Interpreting electrical drawings

There are five types of electrical drawings. These are as follows:

1. Block diagrams
2. Circuit diagrams
3. General assembly diagrams
4. Schematic diagrams
5. Wiring diagrams

Block diagrams

This is a useful way to forward an idea without the need for technical detail. Block diagrams provide a means of focusing on potential problem areas and enable formal planning to be carried out at a later stage.

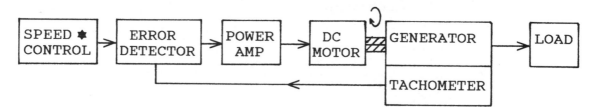

A block diagram for a motor speed control.

Circuit diagrams

Electrical circuit diagrams use simple graphical symbols (BS 3939) to represent components, accessories and appliances, and to show the way in which they are interconnected. For example, consider the illustration below. Wiring is shown as vertical and horizontal lines and the graphical symbols are those recommended by British Standards. Custom-made graphical symbols should not be used as they cause confusion.

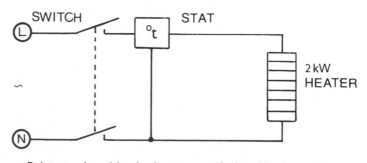

Point-to-point wiring is shown as vertical and horizontal lines as recommended by British Standards.

General assembly diagrams

This type of diagram is often known as a **physical layout diagram** and shows in exact detail how the components, accessories and appliances are to be arranged. Each component part is drawn, labelled and sometimes numbered in proportion to size.

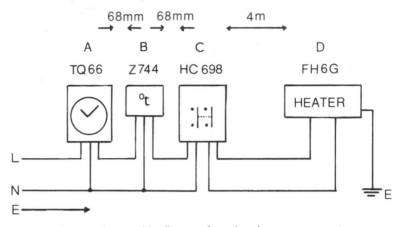

A general assembly diagram for a heating arrangement.
A = time clock; B = room thermostat; C = control switch; D = heater.

Schematic diagrams

Schematic diagrams use BS 3939 graphical symbols and are usually drawn with one line to represent cabling as shown here.

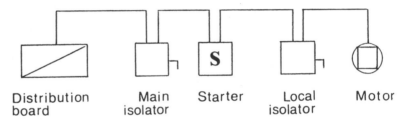

A typical schematic diagram showing the wiring arrangement serving a single phase motor.

Wiring diagrams

Electric wiring diagrams show point-to-point wiring and interconnections for an installation. Wherever possible, BS 3939 graphical symbols should be used but those not conforming with the British Standards' directive must be clearly labelled to avoid confusion.

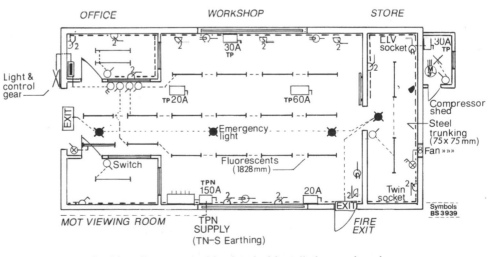

A wiring diagram, used in electrical installation engineering,
provides information for the proposed installation.

Types of electrical cable

There are many different types of electrical cable used in industry.

Cable	Insulation used	Maximum voltage	Use
PVC insulated and sheathed	PVC/PVC	600 V	Domestic and commercial installations
Mineral insulated (MI)	Magnesium oxide (MgO), sometimes called magnesia	500 and 750 V	Critical circuits, alarm systems, boiler houses, hazardous situations, etc.
High-voltage underground	Cross-linked polyethylene (XLPE)	500 kV	National Grid transmission cables
Steel wire armoured	PVC/PVC	500 V core to core	Low-voltage mains distribution and control circuits
Multi-core (tinned steel wire braid covered with clear plastic sheath)	PVC	300/500 V	Factories or where oil, grease or petroleum products are used
Heavy-duty trailing cable	Ethylene propylene rubber (EPR)	450/750 V	Cranes, heavy-duty welding, gantry lifting machinery, etc.
Single core (multi-stranded)	PVC	600 V	General industrial wiring, conduit and trunking installations
Industrial flexible cables	Tough synthetic rubber sheathing	300/500 V	Industry, agricultural workshops, factory inspection lamps and machines
Fire-resistant cables	Low smoke zero halogen (LSZH)	600 V	Fire detection and alarm installations, emergency lighting systems, damp environments
Co-axial	PVC and solid polyethylene (PE)	–	Television and video recorders connecting leads, aerial leads, extra low voltage data transmission
Flexible cords	PVC/PVC	600 V	Electrical appliances, hand inspection lamps, pendant drops, temporary lighting arrangements, serving immersion heater elements (heat-resistant type)
Twin, flat rubber sheathed with no current protective conductor	Rubber/rubber	600 V	Festoon lighting arrangements, decorative outside lighting schemes of a temporary nature

Types of cable other than those given in the table include:

- Welding cables
- Telephone cables
- Cables used in mining
- Street lighting cables
- Well-water cables serving pump motors
- Passenger and goods lift cables
- Arctic grade cables
- Cables used for television cameras
- Data transmission cables
- Fibre optic cables (using light amplification by the stimulated emission of radiation – laser)

Cables must only be used for the purpose intended. Never exceed the maximum voltage and current rating if over-heating and total break-down is to be avoided.

Segregation of circuits

The *Wiring Regulations* require all electrical 'mains' voltage cabling, classified as a **Category 1 Circuit**, to be segregated from telecommunication, sound distribution, intruder alarm, bell and data transmission **Category 2 Circuits**. Fire detection, alarm and emergency lighting arrangements are known as **Category 3 Circuits** and must be routed separately from other categories of circuit. Further information can be obtained from the *Wiring Regulations*.

| Exercise 1.6 | *Conducting and insulating materials* |

1. Name three good conductors of electricity in order of conductivity.

2. Indicate in the space below whether the following statement is true or false: a milliammeter is wired in parallel with the supply voltage.

3. Indicate in the space below whether the following statement is true or false: block diagrams are a useful guide when planning a project from an original idea.

4. List two uses for heavy-duty trailing cable and where it might be used.

5. For this exercise you will be given three coloured-coded resistors of a manageable size.

   (a) Demonstrate to your assessor that you can identify the value of each resistor and its tolerance rating by observing the colour code printed on its side.
   (b) Check the value of each resistor using a multimeter set to a suitable scale. (Remember to check the instrument first.)
   (c) State whether each resistor falls within the tolerance level allowed by the manufacturer.

$$\pm \text{ Value allowed} = \frac{\text{Declared tolerance level}}{100} \times \frac{\text{Colour coded value}}{1}$$

   (d) Record your answers in the space provided.

Resistor	Colour code	Colour coded value	Multimeter value	Is the tolerance level correct?
A				
B				
C				

6. For this exercise you will require the following:

   • A 24 volt isolated supply
   • A multimeter
   • A 20 amp double pole switch
   • A suitable load (up to 12 ohms and 2.5 amp current rating)
   • Insulated wire (for example, 0.5 mm²)
   • Mechanical connectors (rated at 5 amp)

   (a) Form a simple circuit as illustrated on p. 20. (See the first three illustrations.)
   (b) Demonstrate to your assessor that you are able to carry out the following tests:

Test 1 – The value of the voltage supplied.

Test 2 – The current flowing in the circuit.

Test 3 – The total resistance of the load placed in circuit.

Test 4 – The continuity of the circuit when the switch has been placed in the 'open' position.

Voltage recorded:

Current in amps:

Resistance of load:

State briefly how the continuity of the circuit was tested:

7. For this exercise you will be given three electrical appliances that are not served with electronic components (for example, electric drill, soldering iron, a small electric fire, etc.). Each appliance will be a **Category 1** appliance.

  (a) Demonstrate to your assessor that you are able to carry out an insulation test using three Category 1 appliances as examples.
  (b) The test should be made in the following sequence with the appliance switched to the 'ON' position.

    Test 1 – Between the **live** and **neutral** pins of the plug.
    Test 2 – Between the **live** pin of the plug and the **frame** of the appliance.
    Test 3 – Between the **neutral** pin of the plug and the **frame** of the appliance.

  (c) Record your results in the table provided.

Appliance:	
Value of Test 1:	
Value of Test 2:	
Value of Test 3:	*Overall Pass/Fail?*
Appliance:	
Value of Test 1:	
Value of Test 2:	
Value of Test 3:	*Overall Pass/Fail?*
Appliance:	
Value of Test 1:	
Value of Test 2:	
Value of Test 3:	*Overall Pass/Fail?*

8. For this exercise you will be shown six types of electrical cables each of which will be labelled with a letter of the alphabet.

  (a) Demonstrate to your assessor that you are able to match the six samples provided with the six examples described in the table on p. 28.
  (b) Write down your answer in the blank space provided.

    Example A is   and is used for
    Example B is   and is used for
    Example C is   and is used for
    Example D is   and is used for
    Example E is   and is used for
    Example F is   and is used for

9. For this exercise you will be given three different types of capacitors.

  (a) Demonstrate to your assessor that you are able to identify the following types of capacitors.

- **Capacitor 1** Fixed capacitor (non-polarised)
- **Capacitor 2** Trimmer capacitor
- **Capacitor 3** Variable capacitor

(b) Suggest a use for each type of capacitor reviewed.

(c) Write down your answer in the table provided.

Capacitor reference number	Type of capacitor	Suggested use
1.		
2.		
3.		

10. For this exercise you will be given two different values of coloured-coded capacitors.

   (a) Demonstrate to your assessor that you are able to calculate the value of each capacitor.

   (b) Write your answers in the spaces provided.

   Value obtained: Capacitor 1

   List of colours viewed from top to bottom:

   Value obtained:

   Tolerance rating as a percentage:

   Working voltage:

   Value obtained: Capacitor 2

   List of colours viewed from top to bottom:

   Value obtained:

   Tolerance rating as a percentage:

   Working voltage:

11. For this exercise you will be provided with a multimeter and three 1 watt mixed value carbon composition resistors.

   (a) Write the resistor colour bands of each resistor and the number the colour represents by completing the appropriate columns in the table provided.

   (b) Write down the value of each resistor in Column 4.

   (c) Write down the tolerance percentage of each resistor.

   (d) Check each resistor value with your multimeter and write down the result.

   (e) Finally, calculate whether the declared tolerance range is correct and write the word YES or NO in the last column.

Components	Band 1 colour/value	Band 2 colour/value	Band 3 colour/value	Declared value in ohms	Band 4 tolerance percentage	Multimeter value	Is the percentage tolerance correct?
First resistor							
Second resistor							
Third resistor							

Electrical distribution

In Britain we have the choice of two principal electrical supply systems to cater for our power requirements:

1. Single phase and neutral supply
2. Three phase and neutral supply

There are others, but these are of a specialised nature and therefore will not be reviewed here.

Single phase and neutral supply

This type of supply is produced for domestic and light commercial use providing a nominal **230 volts** when measured between the **live** and **neutral** conductors. Also 230 volts can be registered between the live conductor and the **Supply Authority's earth** conductor.

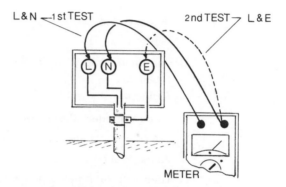

Testing for voltage between the live conductor and neutral and between the live conductor and earth.

In urban areas the **current protective conductor** serving the main electrical distribution centre is connected to the **protective metal sheath** of the Supply Authority's incoming cable. This in turn is is connected to the '**star-point**' of the local community transformer. A **fault current** occurring between the 'live' and protective conductor would have the same result as if the 'live' conductor had touched the neutral conductor. In either case a current protective device would be brought into play.

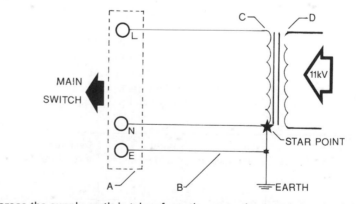

In urban areas the supply earth is taken from the protective metal sheath of the supply cable.
A = electrical mains intake position; B = the supply company's cable sheath (earth);
C = the supply transformer; D = the 11 000 volt side of the supply transformer.
L = live; N = neutral; E = earth.

Three phase and neutral supply

Three phase and neutral supplies are used for industry and commerce. The supply comprises three live conductors, known as L1, L2, and L3, but these are often referred to as **red phase, yellow phase** and **blue phase**. They are accompanied by one neutral conductor.

Measuring between any phase and neutral or earth will provide a value of 230 volts AC, and a value of 400 volts will be obtained when measuring between any combination of phases. As with a single phase supply the electrical earth conductor is connected to the star point of the local community transformer (as shown here).

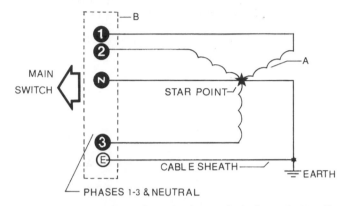

The electrical earth originates from the 'star-point' of supply transformer.
At the consumer's end the supply earth is taken from the cable sheath
of the incoming supply cable. A = common or star point of the windings;
B = the supply authority's fuses and termination point; 1 = red phase;
2 = yellow phase; 3 = blue phase; N = neutral; E = earth.

DC and AC

Direct current (DC)

An electric current in which the flow is always in one direction and does not vary in value is known as **direct current** (DC). Unlike alternating current (AC), DC voltages can be stored in **primary** and **secondary cells** (flash-light batteries and accumulators) and used for powering portable appliances such as torches, electric fences, mobile phones and field soldering irons, etc.

A nominal voltage of 220 volts DC plotted against time would appear as illustrated here.

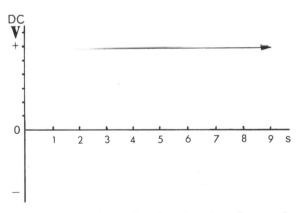

A direct current voltage plotted against time. S, seconds.

Alternating current (AC)

A flow of electricity which reverses its direction at regular frequency is known as **alternating current** (AC). AC voltage is constantly changing its magnitude and direction many times a second. When a maximum voltage has been reached, it will decrease to zero and then climb to a maximum voltage in the **opposite** direction. This transitional period, from positive to negative voltages, is known as a **cycle** and the number of cycles per second represents the **frequency** of the supply. The frequency of an alternating current is measured in **hertz** and throughout the United Kingdom power is generated at 50 hertz (Hz) per second.

Unlike DC, alternating current is continually varying in value, as shown here where voltage is plotted against time.

An alternating voltage plotted against time.

The effect of AC and DC supplies upon components

The table below shows the effect of AC and DC current on common components.

Component	Effect of AC voltage	Effect of DC voltage
Capacitor	Applying an AC voltage to a capacitor will cause the plates to charge and discharge many times a second. This produces a resistance called **reactance** within the circuit. Applying an AC voltage to a capacitor.	The positive plate will attract an electron flow from the negative plate until the voltage across the capacitor is equal to that of the supply. Disconnecting will leave the capacitor in a fully charged condition. 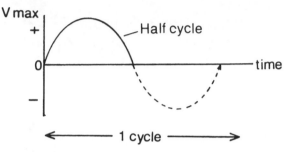 Applying a DC voltage to a capacitor.
Induction coil	A concentrated magnetic field will be generated. If used as a ballast serving a fluorescent fitting, it will limit current flow to the lamp; without this the operational life of the lamp would be reduced.	When an induction coil is connected to a rapid make-and-break device several thousand **pulsed volts** will be produced within a **secondary coil** attached but not physically connected to the induction coil. For example, spark plug voltage in a motor car. It will allow DC current to flow within the induction coil. It will not limit current flow.
Transformer	Will reduce or increase alternating voltage without the frequency of the supply being altered. **Isolating transformers** wil provide the same voltage as applied (230 V in – 230 V out). The secondary voltage is isolated from the electrical mains.	A strong **magnetic field** would be produced within the primary winding. No voltage would be induced into the secondary winding. If the applied DC voltage is high, damage will occur by overheating.

Series and parallel circuits

Series circuits

A circuit is said to be connected in **series formation** when the voltage applied is **shared** between each of the individual loads. Removing an individual component will stop current flow; for example, think of Christmas tree lights!

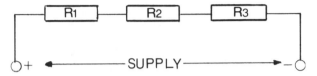

Resistors connected in series formation: R_1 = 10 ohms; R_2 = 20 ohms; R_3 = 30 ohms.

The total value of resistors wired in series formation can be calculated by using the following expression:

$$R_t = R_1 + R_2 + R_3 \ldots$$

where R_t is the total resistance in ohms
   R_1, R_2 and R_3 are the individual resistances in ohms

The following problem shows an example of using this expression:
Problem:
Calculate the total resistance of the series formation circuit shown in the figure above.
Solution:
Using the expression,

$$R_t = R_1 + R_2 + R_3$$

and substituting for known values,

$$R_t = 10 + 20 + 30$$

$$R_t = 60 \text{ ohms}$$

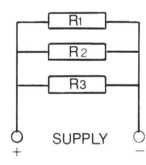

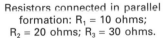

Resistors connected in parallel formation: R_1 = 10 ohms; R_2 = 20 ohms; R_3 = 30 ohms.

Parallel circuits

A circuit is said to be connected in **parallel formation** when the load components are connected side-by-side and their service leads are joined together. The voltage is not shared as with series circuits but is common to each component.
   The total value of resistors wired in parallel formation can be calculated by using the following expression:

$$\frac{1}{R_t} = \frac{1}{R_1} + \frac{1}{R_2} + \frac{1}{R_3} \ldots$$

where R_t is the total resistance of the parallel circuit
   R_1, R_2 and R_3 are the individual resistance values

For example, consider the following:
Problem:
Calculate the total resistance of the parallel circuit shown in the figure above.
Solution:
Using the expression,

$$\frac{1}{R_t} = \frac{1}{R_1} + \frac{1}{R_2} + \frac{1}{R_3}$$

and substituting for known values,

$$\frac{1}{R_t} = \frac{1}{10} + \frac{1}{20} + \frac{1}{30}$$

Selecting a common multiple (60) and working through,

$$\frac{1}{R_t} = \frac{}{60}$$

First 60 divided by 10 is 6, and 6 multiplied by 1 is 6, and so on . . .

$$\frac{1}{R_t} = \frac{6 + 3 + 2}{60}$$

$$\frac{1}{R_t} = \frac{11}{60}$$

Cross-multiplying and bringing R_t to the left-hand side of the equation,

$$R_t \times 11 = 60 \times 1$$

Dividing both sides of the equation by 11 to write the equation in terms of R_t,

$$R_t = \frac{60}{11}$$

$$R_t = 5.45 \text{ ohms}$$

The answer will always be smaller than the smallest value component serving a parallel formation circuit. All the components in the series circuit are the same value as those in the parallel circuit. But the total resistance obtained from the two worked examples are different.

The total resistance of a parallel circuit that has **two** known values can be calculated using the following expression:

$$R_t = \frac{R_1 \times R_2}{R_1 + R_2}$$

Exercise 1.7

Distribution, parallel and series circuits, and Ohm's Law

1. Indicate in the space provided whether the following statement is true or false: DC current continually varies in value but the frequency is electrically stable.

2. Calculate (a) the total resistance of six 10 ohm resistors placed in series formation and (b) the current drawn from the circuit when connected to a 120 volt DC supply.

3. Calculate the total resistance of six 10 ohm resistors placed in parallel formation and the current drawn from the circuit when connected to a 120 volt DC supply. Round your answer up to the nearest decimal place.

4. For this exercise you will require the following:

- Four different value resistors (preferably between 10 and 100 ohms at 12 watt power rating)
- Plastic insulated mechanical connectors (5 amp rated)
- A multimeter (a digital model would be preferred)

(a) Demonstrate to your assessor that you are able to place the four chosen resistors in parallel formation and measure their total resistance by use of a multimeter. A check should be made to see that the instrument works correctly and that there is no damage to the casing or leads.

(b) Show your assessor how resistors are wired in series formation using the mechanical connectors provided and measure the total formation of the group.

(c) Write down your answers in the space provided.

Total resistance of the four resistors in parallel formation:

Total resistance of the four resistors in series formation:

5. For this exercise you will require the following:

- Three 22 ohm, 12 watt resistors
- A small isolating switch
- A multimeter (a digital model would be preferred)
- Insulated mechanical connectors
- A 24 volt isolated supply
- Insulated wire and tools

(a) Arrange the three 22 ohm resistors in series formation using mechanical connectors and tools provided.

(b) Demonstrate to your assessor that you are able to carry out the following tasks:

1. Measure the total resistance of the grouped series resistors using a multimeter; and log.
2. Safely connect the grouped resistors to a 24 volt isolated supply via a simple control switch.
3. Measure the current flowing through the circuit using a multimeter when the control switch is placed in the 'ON' position; and log.
4. With the control switch placed in the 'OFF' position, measure the exact voltage supplied to the circuit using the multimeter; and log.
5. Using Ohm's Law calculate the power generated in watts.
6. Demonstrate that you are also able to calculate the power generated in watts in terms of voltage and resistance.

(c) Write down your answers in the spaces provided.

1. Total resistance of the series circuit:

2. Total current flowing through the circuit:

3. Exact voltage recorded with the switch in the 'OFF' position:

4. Power generated in watts: Expression used:

5. Power generated in watts in terms of voltage and resistance:

Expression used:

| Exercise 1.8 | *The effects of AC and DC supplies upon components* |

1. Indicate in the space provided whether the following statement is true or false: An induction coil will produce several thousand pulsed volts from its secondary winding providing there is a pulsed low voltage DC supply serving the primary winding.

2. For this exercise you will be given a 230 volt primary winding step-down transformer suitably wired and attached to a 13 amp plug fitted with a 3 amp fuse. You will also require the following:

   • A multimeter capable of both AC and DC low voltage measurement
   • A screwdriver

   Demonstrate to your assessor that you are able to successfully carry out the following exercise:

   (a) Place the plug serving the transformer into a suitable AC **switched socket outlet** switched to the 'OFF' position.
   (b) Remove the low voltage terminal cover serving the transformer. Step-down transformers are generally served with three mechanical 'screw' terminals providing an output for three optional voltages.
   (c) Switch ON the transformer at the socket outlet.
   (d) Switch the multimeter to a low voltage AC range; measure and log the following in the spaces provided:

   Test 1 – The voltage across the **outer** terminals
   Test 2 – The voltage across the **left-hand** terminal and the **middle** terminal
   Test 3 – The voltage across the **right-hand** terminal and the **middle** terminal

   The voltage recorded from **Test 1**:

   The voltage recorded from **Test 2**:

   The voltage recorded from **Test 3**:

   What conclusions do you draw from this exercise?

3. This exercise is similar to the last except that direct current electricity will be used instead of alternating current. For this exercise the following will be required:

   • A multimeter capable of both AC and DC low voltage measurement
   • A screwdriver
   • A 230 volt primary winding step-down transformer
   • A switched low voltage DC power source suitably fused

   Demonstrate to your assessor that you are able to successfully carry out the following exercise and draw the correct conclusions.

   (a) First remove the plug serving the transformer from the socket outlet.
   (b) Disconnect the flexible conductors serving the 13 amp plug.
   (c) Connect the disconnected flexible conductors to the terminals serving a low voltage DC power source but first ensure that the DC power has been switched 'OFF'.
   (d) Once the conductors have been safely terminated, switch 'ON' the DC power source.
   (e) Measure and log the following in the space provided:
   Test 1 – Measure the value of the incoming DC voltage.
   Test 2 – Measure the voltage across the **outer** terminals serving the low voltage side of the transformer.
   Test 3 – Measure the voltage across the **left-hand** terminal and the **middle** terminal serving the low voltage side of the transformer.
   Test 4 – Measure the voltage across the **right-hand** terminal and the **middle** terminal serving the low voltage side of the transformer.

The voltage recorded from **Test 1**:

The voltage recorded from **Test 2**:

The voltage recorded from **Test 3**:

The voltage recorded from **Test 4**:

What conclusions do you draw from this exercise?

Protection for AC and DC circuits

The following devices give protection against **overcurrent** and **short circuit** conditions.

- Fuses
- Circuit breakers
- Thermal overcurrent devices

Fuses

These can be one of the following three types:

1. High breaking capacity (HBC) cartridge fuses
2. Rewirable (semi-enclosed) fuses
3. Cartridge fuses (the type fitted to 13 amp plugs)

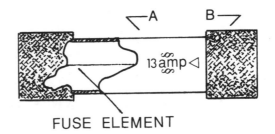

FUSE ELEMENT

Cartridge fuses to BS 1361 and BS 1362.
A = ceramic body; B = brass end caps.

Miniature circuit breakers (MCB)

There are three types of MCBs, all of which are manufactured to the requirements of British Standard (BS) 3871.

1. Magneto-hydraulic
2. Assisted bimetal
3. Thermal and magnetic

Moulded case circuit breaker (MCCB)

There are two types of MCCBs, both of which are manufactured to the requirements of BS 3871.

1. Thermal magnetic
2. Magnetic

While both fuses and MCBs are used to protect final circuits, MCCBs are designed to protect main supply cables serving sub-mains distribution centres. The difference between MCCBs and MCBs is their physical size (MCCBs are larger) and their current-carrying and short-circuit characteristics.

For additional details of overcurrent protection methods, see p. 78.

Thermal overcurrent devices

A widely accepted method of overcurrent protection is the **thermal overload relay**, which when coupled to an electric motor starter forms an integral part of the unit.

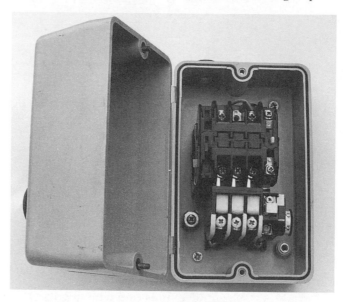

Overcurrent protection serving an electric motor starter.

The overcurrent protection device is made from three independent heater elements, which are connected in series formation with the supply phases (L1, L2, and L3). If an overcurrent occurs the heating elements warm up a bimetal strip, which in turn opens a small integral relay. The relay acts as a switch to the electromagnetic coil, which, once opened, isolates electricity supplying the coil. Under these conditions the coil will de-energise and will switch off the supply to the electric motor.

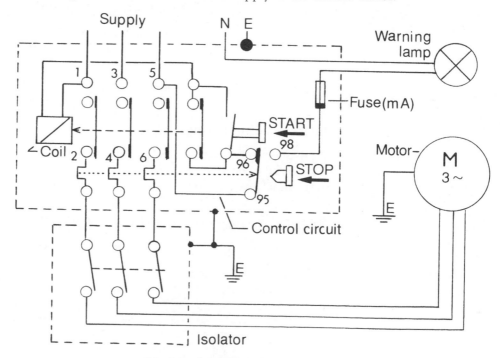

Principle of the thermal overcurrent relay.

Each of the three heating elements are coiled around an insulated and anchored bimetal strip, which has been allowed freedom of movement at one end as shown here.

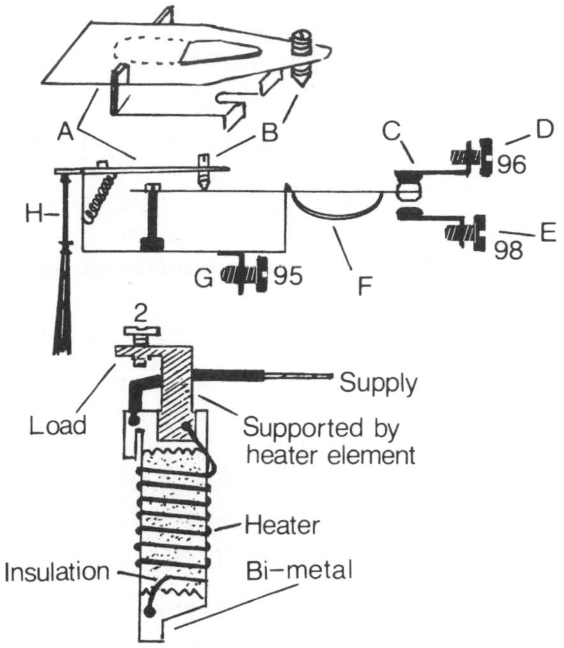

Mechanical principles of the thermal overload relay.
A = tripping plate; B = adjustment screw;
C = relay contacts; D = coil circuit terminal 96;
E = coil circuit terminal 98 for remote
'overload tripped' indicator; F = sprung copper strip;
G = coil circuit terminal 95; H = pivoted lever
attached to a linear slide integrally linked
to the bimetal of the overload heaters.

Miniature bimetal devices

Miniature bimetal overload devices are often attached to the body of an electric motor rated under **0.75 kW** (750 watts). Two types are available. One is designed with a small heating element wired in series formation with the overload's simple switching arrangement. The other type is placed in the supply line to protect the motor both thermally and from overcurrent situations. Both models are equipped with a small current carrying **bimetal strip** forged from spring metal. Some models are designed to be manually reset. Others will snap back to their original position when cool.

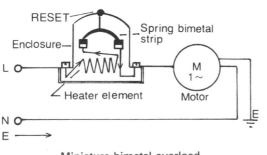

Miniature bimetal overload
with a built-in heater element.

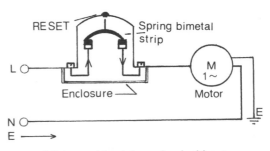

Miniature bimetal overload without
a built-in heater element.

Checking the operating voltage of an appliance

It is important that the operating voltage is correct when connecting or using an appliance.

An electric motor will burn out or shut down due to overcurrent if the applied voltage is either too great or too low. A 110 volt inspection lead bulb would be destroyed in milliseconds if used on a 230 volt circuit.

The following points can be used to check the operating voltage of an appliance:

- Shape and colour of the plug (for example, yellow 110 volt, blue 230 volt and red 400 volt).
- Colour and size of the lead (for example, a heavy yellow lead would be rated at 110 volts).
- Appliance data plate details showing the voltage, amperage and power of the appliance.
- Type of installation serving the appliance (for example, single phase at 230 volts).

If confusion remains, the resistance of the appliance can be checked with a multimeter. For example, 110 volt 1 kW (1000 watt) electric fire would have an electrical resistance of 12 ohms compared with approximately 53 ohms for the same wattage fire designed to operate from a 230 volt system.

Preventing injury

The table below lists safety measures designed to prevent personal injury in the workplace.

Part(s) of the body	Means of protection
Head	Hard hat
Ears	Ear protection, industrial ear plugs
Eyes	Goggles, safety spectacles
Face	Visor or transparent face shield
Lungs	Dust mask, respirator
Hands	Barrier cream, gloves, hand protection
Knees	Knee pads
Feet	Steel-capped boots or shoes
General	1. Safety overalls for workshop duties
	2. Protective clothing for special duties
	3. Hair nets when testing out moving parts
	4. Harness belt when working at height
	5. High-visibility garments (for example, fluorescent waistcoats) when work is carried out outside in public places
	6. Life-jackets when work is carried out at sea or near deep water
	7. Industrial apron and battery gloves for use with battery acid
	8. Seat belts when travelling in company transport

Exercise 1.9 — Methods of circuit protection

1. Indicate in the space provided whether the following statement is true or false: Semi-enclosed and high-breaking capacity fuses are both cartridge type fuses.

2. Indicate in the space provided whether the following statement is true or false: A thermal overload relay is designed for the protection of an electric motor and its circuit.

3. Indicate in the space provided whether the following statement is true or false:
Moulded case circuit breakers are usually used to protect electrical cables serving sub-main installations.

4. Indicate in the space provided whether the following statement is true or false:
The two miniature bimetal overcurrent protection devices reviewed have small current carrying bimetal strips forged from spring metal with a small electrical heating element wired in series formation with the overload's switching assembly.

5. For this exercise you will be shown three itemised common overcurrent protection devices.

   (a) Demonstrate to your assessor that you are able to identify each device.
   (b) Suggest a practical use for each device and record your comments in the blank table provided.

Overcurrent device	Type	Practical use	Typical operating voltage
A			
B			
C			

6. For this exercise you will be provided with a simple heating element.
The power rating in watts will be given to you by your tutor.

   (a) Demonstrate by use of an ohm or multimeter that you are able to determine that the element provided is best suited for one of the following voltages:

   1. 400 volts
   2. 240 volts
   3. 230 volts
   4. 110 volts
   5. 50 volts

   (b) Use Ohm's Law and variations of Ohm's Law to determine the answer in the space provided. Please show calculations.

The element provided: watts

The resistance of the element: ohms

Best suited for: volt supply

Working safely with electrical equipment

Some of the hazards that can occur when using electrical equipment are:

- Eye damage caused by flying masonry nails.
- Shock due to wrongly assuming conductors are dead.
- Electrical burns caused by flash-over conditions.
- Lung damage due to airborne asbestos dust while drilling or cutting asbestos products.
- Shock caused by mishandling capacitors.
- Damage, such as crushing, rupturing or snagging, occurring to extension leads and temporary cable runs, which have been badly positioned.
- Accidents caused by delaying the repair of broken or damaged electrical plant.
- Damage to the wrist caused by hand-held drilling machines seizing in stubborn masonry.
- Burns, caused by hand-held rewirable fuses rupturing.
- Shock caused by frayed or damaged flexes serving power-tools.
- Death or injury caused by faulty or damaged appliances.
- Burns or flash-overs caused by wrist-watches or bracelets worn when work is carried out on live equipment or secondary cells (batteries).
- Mild shocks leading to falls, due to capacitance stored in long cable runs.
- Respiratory problems when work is carried out in roof spaces lined with old fibreglass thermal insulation.
- Crushed toes caused by misuse of large wooden cable drums.
- Splinters, cuts and scratches caused when handling large wooden cable drums.
- Electric shock caused by touching rain-drenched wooden distribution poles.
- Sickness when electrical work is done in grain storage silos, poultry farms or piggeries. Always use a suitable face mask.
- Explosion, caused by smoking in an unventilated battery charging room.
- Strained back due to lifting heavy electrical accessories and appliances.
- Electric shock caused through tiredness, brought about by a long working day.

Reducing the risks

The following list suggests ways to minimise possible dangers when working with electrical equipment:

1. Think ahead at all times; be aware of any problems.
2. Wear the correct type of protective clothing.
3. Work accompanied on live mains.
4. Use only 110 volt power tools when working on site.
5. Replace frayed or mechanically damaged flexes immediately.
6. Regularly inspect plugs serving hand-held power tools for damage, loose or disconnected conductors.
7. Remove personal jewellery when work is carried out on 'live' equipment.
8. Use the correct type of face mask when working with or dismantling asbestos. Also use a face mask when using a masonry disc cutter or chasing walls or when working in a roof space lined with fibreglass.
9. Wear eye protection when hammering home masonry nails.
10. Be sure you are physically capable of lifting and carrying heavy loads – if not, seek assistance.
11. Keep tools sharp and well ground. Blunt tools are dangerous.

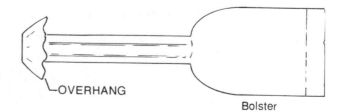

OVERHANG

Bolster

Trim any metallic overhang around the impact area of a cold chisel or bolster.

12. Protect against the danger of earth leakage currents by using a 'plug-in' **residual current device** (RCD) that has a tripping current of 30 milliamps.
13. Power-tools must be handled correctly if muscular strain is to be avoided. Never overstretch when drilling hard masonry.
14. Report any possible hazards to an appropriate person before starting work.
15. Wear industrial gloves to handle **refactory bricks** when building a night storage heater and never carry more than you can manage.
16. Avoid over-accommodating multi-socket adaptors.

Avoid over-use of multi-socket adaptors.

17. Never use 230 volt power-tools under site conditions. It is much safer to use 110 volt tools from a 110 volt power source.
18. Never overload or exceed the voltage for which a cable is designed.
19. Cables should not be placed underground unless specifically designed for that purpose.
20. Treat charged capacitors with respect. Do not misuse.
21. Extention leads must be fully unwound from the reel in order to prevent overheating.
22. Do not day-dream; it could lead to an accident.
23. Use suitable protective clothing and eye protection when working with acid and secondary cells.
24. Always make sure that a battery room is well ventilated.
25. After handling lead acid accumulators always wash your hands thoroughly, especially before meals.

Coping with an electric shock victim

An electric fault path can travel through an operative to earth where there is no current protective conductor to protect from such conditions. Sometimes an electric shock can result in death as the electrical resistance of the human body is very low compared with that of an insulator. Children are most at risk as their body resistance is much lower than an adult.

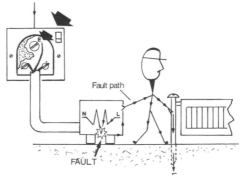

Fault path taken in the absence of a current protective conductor.

Self-help

Hazards arising from the use of electrical equipment can be reduced through law making (legislation), such as the **Health and Safety at Work Act** (HASAWA). **British Standards** (BS) and various **Codes of Practice** are also helpful.

Above all, self-help is essential. Always check inspection leads and extension cables for problems. Inspect the plugs serving the plant and equipment for loose wires or damage to the moulded plastic. Portable appliances should be tested using the **portable appliance test** (PAT) at regular intervals and the results logged for future reference. Check the installation at least once a year in an industrial environment making sure there are no earthing or insulation problems associated with the fixed wiring. Only use 110 volt and extra-low voltage equipment whenever practical. Battery-operated drills are much safer to use than 230 volt mains power-drills; use them wherever possible.

Treatment for electric shock

Finding an electric shock victim can be quite frightening. The golden rule is to act quickly but not panic.

When breathing stops due to an accident caused through direct contact with electricity, brain damage will probably occur within three minutes.

It is vital that air is forced into the casualty's lungs until he or she is able to breath normally again.

This is carried out by **mouth-to-mouth resuscitation** and consists of several important stages. These are fully dealt with on pages 83–4. A brief list in summary form is given below:

1. Switch off the source of current and remove the victim from the exposed conductive part.
2. Lay the victim on his or her back and open the victim's mouth.
3. Remove any debris from inside the mouth.
4. Check for breathing.
5. Find and feel the pulse at the neck.
6. If both breathing and pulse are present turn the casualty to the recovery position as shown on p. 84.

When the breathing has stopped

7. If there is evidence of a pulse but breathing has stopped, start **artificial ventilation**.
8. Pinch the victim's nose and blow into his or her mouth at the rate of 10 breaths a minute (one breath every six seconds).
9. Check the pulse after every 10 breaths.
10. When breathing is considered to be normal, place your patient in the recovery position and call the first aid centre.

Illustrations can be seen on pages 83–4.

Exercise 1.10

Health and safety with electricity in mind

1. State two common hazards associated with people handling large wooden cable drums.

2. How can an operative be protected against damaging earth leakage currents when using a factory extension lead?

3. Why is it wise to completely unwind a reeled extension lead?

4. Why is it considered best to remove personal jewellery before work is carried out on electrical equipment or lead acid secondary cells?

5. What type of protection would be worn when working in an old roof space lined with decaying fibreglass thermal insulation?

6. For this exercise you will be provided with a box in which indexed industrial safety wear has been placed.

   (a) Demonstrate to your assessor that you are able to seek out and identify the following items:

   - Industrial gloves
   - Face mask (general purpose)
   - Hard hat
   - Industrial goggles (general purpose)
   - Plastic face shield

   (b) Discuss with your assessor under what circumstances and why they are worn.
   (c) Please record your comments in the table below.

Safety wear reference	Name of safety wear	Where worn	Why worn
A			
B			
C			
D			
E			

An exercise covering treatment for electric shock may be found on p. 84.

Electrical measurements

Electrical test instruments play a vital role in everyday engineering because they are able to provide the user with information that the eye cannot see. As electricity cannot be seen, there is a need for instruments to inform and evaluate developments inside a circuit.

Work-bench testing can be carried out simply and safely by the use of one or more of the commercial instruments readily available to the engineer (see p. 53).

The relationship between current, voltage and resistance

Current and voltage

Voltage may be compared to water pressure inside a service pipe whereas **current** can be described as the flow of water travelling through the pipe. Increasing the size of the pipe will cause greater current flow whereas reducing its size will decrease the flow of water through the pipe.

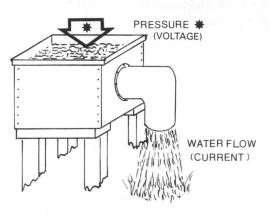

Far less resistance is experienced when the outlet pipe is large.

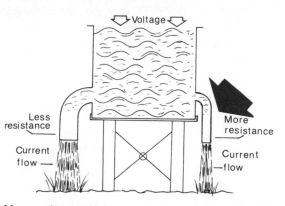

More resistance is experienced when the outlet pipe is small compared with its larger companion.

Electrical current flow is a continuous stream of invisible particles pressurised by the presence of a voltage. When a voltage is measured using a voltmeter electrical pressure is, in fact, being measured, whereas when current is measured with an ammeter the rate of particle flow past any given point is recorded.

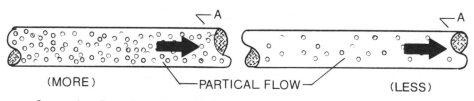

Current is a flow of particles called electrons. The greater the particle flow the greater the current drawn from the circuit. A = current carrying conductor.

Resistance

The resistance of a component or circuit is the opposition that is offered to current flow. Not all material substances offer the same opposition to electrical flow; it depends upon the composition of the material. Imagine running along a well-lit tunnel free from rubbish. No problem! Now fill the tunnel with junk and switch the lights off. The physical resistance experienced makes it far harder to travel the same distance – so it is with electricity when connected to a cable of high resistance.

How elements respond to the flow of electricity in relation to their natural resistance is shown in the table on page 49.

Conductor of electricity	Electrical resistivity based on a scale of 1–100 (1 is very good; 100 is poor)
Aluminium	2.65
Brass	5.00
Bronze	30.00
Copper	1.70
Gold	2.40
Iron (pure)	11.00
Invar	81.00
Lead	21.00
Nickel	59.00
Silver	1.60
Stainless steel	96.00
Steel (mild)	15.00
Tin	11.00
Zinc	5.90

Measuring instruments

Unfortunately, different techniques have to be applied to measure the value of voltage, current, and resistance, together with the power generated in a circuit. It would be much easier if a single method of measurement was available, but this is not possible.

Measuring voltages up to 24 volts DC

Shown here is a simple circuit, comprising:

- A 24 volt DC supply
- An indicator lamp
- A variable resistor

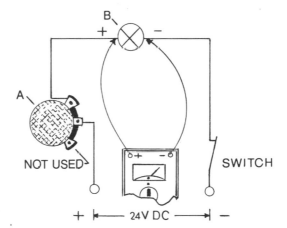

A simple circuit controlled by a variable resistor.
A = 250 ohm, 3 watt rotary resistor; B = 2.8 watt MES base bulb.

This illustrates how voltage may be measured using a standard multimeter. First, switch the multimeter to the voltage range on a suitable setting that will allow 24 volts to be read easily. Remember to take the necessary precautions.

By turning the **variable resistor** to its lowest position, the voltage recorded will be very small and the indicator lamp will appear very dim. Moving the variable resistor to a mid-point position will provide a higher voltage and the lamp will respond by becoming brighter. Turning the variable resistor to its maxium setting will allow a full 24 volts to flow and the indicator lamp will be at its brightest.

Polarity

It is very important to notice the **polarity** when measuring DC voltages. Check that the red coloured lead comes from the **positive** terminal of the test instrument and is placed on the **positive** side of the circuit. A similar check must be made with the negative lead. If the polarity is reversed, the instrument will indicate a **zero** or a **minus** value. This could result in an unfortunate accident if the circuit being worked on was thought to be electrically dead.

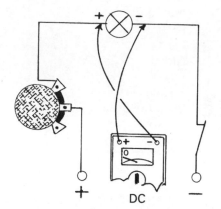

Swapping over the leads (reversing the polarity)
will record a **zero** or **minus** quantity on the meter.

Resistance and power

A typical one-bar electric fire, in schematic form, is connected through a double pole switch to a 230 volt AC supply. To find the power generated, the resistance of the element must first be found, after which **Ohm's Law** will allow the power in watts to be calculated. In practice the following method is used.

First select the correct scale – if necessary by trial and error. Use a multimeter to obtain the value in ohms of the electric fire element. (Always unplug the electric fire from the electrical mains before testing is carried out.) The value in ohms can be obtained by placing a test probe at each end of the electric fire element. When measuring resistance, polarity does not matter; it will make no difference which way the test leads are connected.

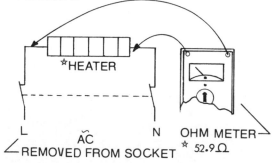

Finding the power generated from a one-bar electric fire
after it has been unplugged from the socket outlet.

Assume a value of 52.9 ohms has been measured. By applying Ohm's Law, the power in watts may be calculated, as may be the current drawn in amps:

$$I = \frac{V}{R} \quad \text{or} \quad \text{Amps} = \frac{\text{Voltage}}{\text{Resistance}}$$

Substituting for known values:

$$I = \frac{230}{52.9}$$

$$I = 4.34783 \text{ amps}$$

The power generated within the circuit can be calculated by referring to the table on p. 6.

$$\text{Power in watts} = I \times V \quad \text{or} \quad I^2 \times R \quad \text{or} \quad \frac{V^2}{R}$$

Substituting for known values:

Power in watts = 4.34783×230 $\quad$ = 1000 watts
Power in watts = $(4.34783)^2 \times 52.9$ = 1000 watts
Power in watts = $\dfrac{(230)^2}{52.9}$ $\quad\quad$ = 1000 watts

In practice this would be classed as a 1 kilowatt electric fire.

Exercise 1.11

Voltage, current and resistance

1. Using your own words, briefly describe what is meant by electrical resistance.

2. Calculate the voltage applied to a circuit generating 2000 watts of power when the current measured is found to be 8.695 amps. Work to the nearest whole number.

3. Why is it necessary to observe correct polarity when measuring DC voltage with a test instrument?

4. Using the blank spaces, **sketch** how the following test instruments are connected in circuit:

Sketch A Testing for voltage
Sketch B Testing for current values
Sketch C Testing for resistance values

Your circuit will comprise the following:

• One battery
• One switch
• Onc indicator lamp

Sketch A $\quad\quad\quad\quad\quad\quad\quad\quad\quad\quad$ Sketch B $\quad\quad\quad\quad\quad\quad\quad\quad\quad\quad$ Sketch C

5. For this exercise you will require the following components:

   • A 24 volt DC power source (minimum rating of 1.0 amp)
   • A round MES bulb rated at 2.8 watt, 24 volt and holder
   • A variable 3 watt (maximum) 250 ohm rotary resistor (unswitched)
   • A single pole switch
   • Approximately 300 mm of 0.5 mm² flexible insulated wire

   Connect the components together as illustrated on p. 49. If you have not been shown how to terminate conductors using soldered joints, then attach two small push-on insulated crimp connectors to the rotary resistor terminals.

   (a) Demonstrate to your assessor that you are competent in measuring voltages up to 24 volts DC.
   (b) Measure the voltage across the indicator lamp when the rotary resistance is at its mid-point position. Describe to your assessor the intensity of the light shining from the bulb.
   (c) Measure the voltage across the indicator lamp when the rotary resistor is at its maximum setting. Describe to your assessor how the light intensity has changed.
   (d) Show your assessor the most suitable test point on the circuit in order to measure voltage.
   (e) Observe the correct polarity of the circuit in relation to the test instrument.
   (f) Correctly select your test instrument and set it to a suitable range.
   (g) Observe all necessary precautions when testing is carried out.

6. For this exercise you will need the following:

   • Two 22 ohm resistors (50 watt, wire wound)
   • A 24 volt DC power source (minimum rating of 2.5 amps)
   • One single pole switch and an ammeter
   • Approximately 300 mm of 0.5 mm² flexible insulated cable

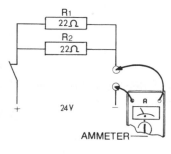

   (a) Connect the components together as shown. If you have not been shown how to use solder, clamp the two resistors together with a mechanical connector.
   (b) Wire the ammeter in circuit as illustrated, keeping the switch in the 'OFF' position until you are ready to test.
   (c) Demonstrate to your assessor that you are able to correctly connect the instrument in circuit to measure current up to 2 amps to an accuracy of 5% when using an analogue meter or 1% if a digital meter is used.
   (d) Choose a suitable point in the circuit for measuring the current. Make sure that the instrument is correctly connected.

7. For this exercise you will require the following:

   • An ohm meter or multimeter
   • Three 10 ohm (2 watt) resistors
   • A work-board
   • Approximately 150 mm or 0.5 mm² insulated wire

   (a) Connect the resistors together as shown on p. 35.
       If you have not been shown how to use solder, clamp the resistors together as illustrated, using mechanical connectors.
   (b) Demonstrate to your assessor that you are able to correctly use an ohm or multimeter to carry out the following tasks:

       (i) Measure the value of each individual resistor (R1, R2 and R3) and compare with the components' declared values. Use the space provided below.
       (ii) Measure the resistance of all three resistors in parallel formation.
            What difference have you noticed? Use the space provided below.

   (c) Rearrange and connect the three resistors in series formation as shown on p. 35.

(d) Demonstrate to your assessor that you can correctly use an ohm meter to measure the total value of all three resistors in series formation to an accuracy of 5%, if an analogue meter is used, or 1% when using a digital meter. Record the value in the space provided below.

(e) Correctly select the test instrument required and check for accuracy.

(f) Choose a suitable test point to carry out resistance measurements.

(b) (i):

(b) (ii):

(d) :

Moving coil meter

This is a very accurate commercial instrument for measuring DC current. It is often used in control panels and electrical workshops as a desk model.

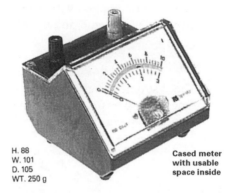

H. 88
W. 101
D. 105
WT. 250 g

Cased meter
with usable
space inside

Moving coil meter. (Reproduced by kind permission of RS Components Ltd.)

Basically a coil of wire is wound around an aluminium former moulded to fit a soft iron cylinder, which is free to rotate. The cylinder is controlled by two phosphor bronze hair springs – one is wound clockwise, the other anticlockwise.

Loading

Many moving coil meters have two scales (volts and amps) for use with voltmeter resistors. Without a suitable shunt (shunts will be dealt with later) moving coil meters are unable to measure high values of current. Listed below are the maximum currents that different stand-alone instruments are able to measure. These currents are known as the **full-scale deflections** of the instruments.

- 50 microamps (millionths of one amp)
- 1 milliamp (one-thousandth of one amp)
- 100 milliamps
- 1 amp

Voltages

Stand-alone DC moving coil voltmeters are often found mounted in control panels or may be seen in workshops as desk models. Listed are five examples of fixed range moving coil meters. The given voltages represent the full-scale deflection of the instrument:

- 0–1 volts
- 0–3 volts
- 0–10 volts
- 0–100 volts
- 0–300 volts

Sensitivity

The sensitivity of this type of instrument depends on the following four points:

1. A large area of coil with many turns
2. A sensitive hair spring
3. A very good permanent magnet
4. The radius of the coil

One practical advantage to be gained by using a moving coil meter is that the measurement scale is evenly spaced and may be read with ease. It may also be used for voltage and current meaurements.

Moving iron meter (repulsion type)

The advantage of this type of instrument is that it may be used on both AC and DC voltages. As the scale is not evenly spaced, the measurement pointer tends to vibrate a little if not equipped with a mechanical damping device. As the scale is not even it is crowded at one end and therefore is not as precise as the moving coil meter.

Operation

The instrument consists of a coil of wire in which two **soft iron formers** are housed. One is fixed to the static mechanism of the instrument while the other is free to rotate. A measurement pointer is fitted and has freedom to move across the scale.

Moving iron meter. (Reproduced by kind permission of RS Components Ltd.)

Moving iron instruments can be designed to record either voltage or current flow. Without an electrical **shunt** mechanism (see below) they are only capable of recording a few milliamps.

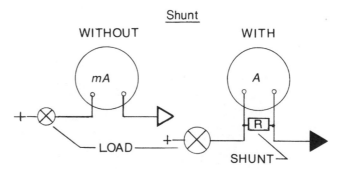

Without a shunt mechanism a moving iron instrument would only be able to record a few milliamps of current.

Loading

Listed are examples of commercial moving iron instruments detailing their maximum full-scale deflection in volts or amps.

Voltmeters

- 0–15 volts
- 0–30 volts
- 0–150 volts
- 0–300 volts
- 0–500 volts

Ammeters

- 100 microamps
- 1 milliamp
- 1 amp
- 5 amps
- 10 amps

Shunts and multipliers

Fitting a low value resistor to a milliammeter will allow a greater current flow to be recorded. The resistor, placed in **parallel** with the coil of the ammeter, allows most of the current to by-pass the delicate windings of the instrument. The small amount of current that enters the meter will record the value of current inside the circuit under test. A resistor used in this way is known as a shunt. Shunts are designed to fit onto the rear of the meter and will accommodate terminal sizes up to 6.5 mm in diameter.

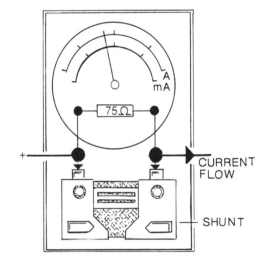

The shunt resistor is placed in parallel with the coil of the instrument.
This illustration is not to scale and has been drawn to show the
relationship between the instrument and the shunt.

Composition

A copper alloy called **manganin** is used in the manufacture of shunts. The alloy conducts electricity well, is not affected by changes in the surrounding temperature and is very reliable.

Multipliers

A **multiplier** is simply a high value resistor placed in series formation with the coil of the voltmeter. This allows the instrument to cope with higher voltages.

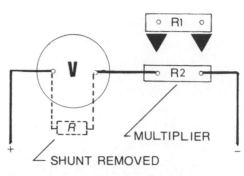

A multiplier is a high valued resistor placed in series formation
with the instrument and allows far higher voltages to be measured.

A resistor may also be used to convert a milliammeter into a voltmeter. By removing
the parallel shunt resistor and placing a suitable resistor in series formation as shown,
higher voltages can be measured. Normally high stability **metal film** resistors known
as **range setting** resistors are used.

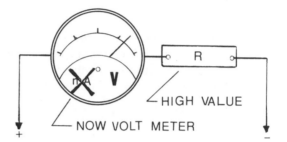

Converting a moving iron meter to record higher voltages.

Analogue and digital instruments

Analogue

Analogue meters have easy-to-read scales and a **taut band movement** in order to
combat everyday knocks and work-bench conditions. A typical bench-type multimeter,
ideally suited for workshop conditions, is shown here.

A multimeter is an ideal instrument for workshop use.
(Reproduced by kind permission of Robin Electronics Ltd.)

Modern 'off-the-shelf' test instruments are now fully electronic and are equipped
with many features including easy-to-handle selector switches to avoid confusion
when different measurements are made. With between 20 and 30 measurement
ranges, the electronic analogue multimeter can be used for many different tasks.
A typical selection would include the following:

- Continuity testing
- AC voltages
- DC voltages
- Resistance values
- AC current
- DC current
- Decibel values
- Instrument battery check

The typical accuracy factor for this type of meter is generally 3–4% of the full scale reading.

Functions

What a multimeter can measure largely depends on the make and model of the instrument concerned. Generally, analogue range multimeters can cope with the following tasks:

1. DC voltages from 150 millivolts to 1500 volts
2. AC voltages from 5 volts to 1500 volts
3. DC current from 50 microamps to 10 amps
4. AC current from 500 microamps to 10 amps
5. Resistance from 20 000 ohms to 2 megohms (two million ohms)
6. Decibel levels from −6 dB to +16 dB

Digital

Digital instruments have a large liquid crystal display (LCD) panel and values are read direct from the screen.

Instruments like these are designed for general purpose use and have many functions, such as:

1. Voltage measurements from millivolts to 400 volts (AC and DC)
2. Frequency up to 2000 Hertz (Hz)
3. Diode test facility
4. Bar graph indicator within the display panel
5. Transistor test facility
6. Continuity testing (audio or visual)
7. Current measurements from 400 microamps to 10 amps (AC and DC)
8. Resistance measurements from 40 ohms to 40 megohms
9. Capacitance measurements from 1 microfarad to 1000 microfarads
10. Low resistance scale from 0.01 ohms

The low resistance scale is particularly useful when fault finding, as values as low as 0.01 can be measured. One disadvantage is that it is possible to mistake the position of the decimal point and read values wrongly.

The accuracy of this type of meter is very good, i.e. between ±0.3 and 2.0% of the reading displayed.

It is wise to store test instruments correctly and safely when not in use, or they may become damaged.

| Exercise 1.12 | *Electrical test instruments* |

1. Using your own words, briefly describe one advantage of choosing a moving iron voltmeter for general bench/workshop use.

2. Which type of meter would be best for measuring low resistance values?

3. How would you prepare a moving coil ammeter to measure a 20 amp load when the full scale reading is only 2 amps?

4. Sketch in the space provided how you would connect a moving iron ammeter to measure current flow in a simple circuit comprising battery, connecting flexes and a low-powered indicator lamp.

5. Sketch in the space provided how you would connect a multimeter set to the DC voltage scale to measure the voltage supplied to a simple circuit comprising battery, connecting flexes, lampholder and lamp.

6. For this exercise you will need the following:

   • One multimeter
   • One 40 watt household lamp
   • One 100 watt household lamp
   • Approximately 160 mm of 0.5 mm² insulated flexible wire
   • One standard lampholder (Bayonet cap)

   (a) Cut the flexible wire in half and suitably remove the insulation from all ends. Terminate both wires in the lampholder.
   (b) Measure the total resistance in ohms of the 40 watt lamp.

   (c) Next measure the total resistance in ohms of the 100 watt lamp.

   (d) What conclusions do you draw from this exercise?

7. For this exercise you will require the following:

- One metre in length of single PVC-insulated 6 mm^2 power cable
- One metre in length of single PVC-insulated 1 mm^2 lighting cable

   (a) Demonstrate to your assessor that you are able to correctly select an instrument to measure the total resistance of 1 metre of 6 mm^2 cable and 1 metre of 1 mm^2 cable.

   (b) Bare the ends of the two lengths of cable to expose the copper conductor to approximately 5 mm in length.

   (c) Using a digital multimeter, set the instrument to the correct scale and measure the total resistance of the heavier cable.

   (d) Next measure the total resistance of the lighter cable.

   (e) What are your conclusions and how do the recorded values compare?

8. For this exercise you will need the following:

- One bench/desk-type **moving iron voltmeter** (full scale deflection of 30 volts)
- One DC power source (no greater than 24 volts)
- One AC power source (no greater than 24 volts)
- Two lengths of 300 mm long 0.5 mm^2 flexible wire (insulated)

   (a) Demonstrate to your assessor that you can use a moving iron voltmeter to correctly measure voltages up to 24 volts AC and DC.

   (b) Record the voltage measured for both the AC and DC supplies.

9. For this exercise the following will be required:

- One bench/desk-type moving coil DC ammeter (full scale deflection of 100 milliamp)
- One work-board
- 600 mm of 0.5 mm^2 flexible insulated cable
- A DC power source no greater than 24 volts
- One 470 ohm vitreous wound, or equivalent, resistor at 2.5 watts
- Small wire connectors (mechanical screw type)
- One single pole switch

   (a) Arrange the load resistor and ammeter in circuit as described previously.

   (b) For the purpose of this exercise use the screw-type connectors provided to form the circuit.

   (c) Demonstrate to your assessor that you are able to connect a moving coil ammeter correctly in circuit to measure current drawn.

(d) Use a DC power source no greater than 24 volts. Connect the load resistor, switch and ammeter in circuit keeping the switch in the 'OFF' position until you are ready to measure the value of current drawn.

(e) Record the value of current measured in the space provided.

Materials used in electrical work

The table below lists in random order, materials used in general electrical engineering and installation work with practical reference notes.

Material used	Status conductor/ non-conductor	Use in electrical work
Mica	Non-conductor	Used as an insulator or as a dielectric in capacitors.
Polyvinylchloride (PVC)	Non-conductor	Used as insulation for conductors. Also used to make electrical conduit, trunking and tray work.
Malleable cast iron	Conductor	Electrical conduit fittings.
Steel and stainless steel	Conductor	Used to make conduit, switchgear, fixing devices and electrical enclosures.
Copper	Conductor	Used to make cables and wires. Also used for switch connections, electrical nuts and bolts, etc.
Aluminium	Conductor	Used in the manufacture of cables and electrical fittings.
Brass	Conductor	Terminals, conduit fittings, nuts and bolts and electrical accessories.
Tungsten	Conductor	Filaments for lamps and bulbs.
Mercury	Conductor	Discharge lamps and tilt-switches serving some types of thermostats.
Moulded plastic	Non-conductor	Appliances, sockets and switches, etc.
Germanium	Semi-conductor	Diodes, transistors, etc.
Silicon	Semi-conductor	Diodes, transistors, etc.
Perspex® (thermoplastic resin)	Non-conductor	Special types of conduit and trunking. Lenses and covers and lids for electrical cabinets, etc.
Ceramics	Non-conductor	Fuses, fuse carriers and high-temperature connectors. Ceramics are also used for some types of insulators.
Manganin (a copper alloy)	Conductor with high electrical resistance	Used in instruments and as resistance wire for many applications (for example, heating appliances).
Magnesium oxide (also known as magnesia)	Non-conductor	Used as an insulator in mineral insulated cables. Magnesia is also used in the production of semi-conductors.
Carbon	Conductor	Used in the production of resistors. Carbon is also used for 'brushes' serving certain types of electric motor. Used for contacts serving special heavy-duty relays. Found also in torch batteries.
Lead and lead alloy	Conductor	Used as a secondary protective sheath for underground cables. The lead sheath also acts as the current protective conductor. Found in some types of re-chargeable batteries. Used as protection and as a current protective conductor for sheathed cable.
Dilute sulphuric acid	Non-conductor	Used in lead-acid accumulators in dilute form.
Glass	Non-conductor	Used in electrical fittings, lamps and bulbs, etc. Optical glass is sometimes used for lenses to serve indicator lamps. Employed for electronic valve envelopes and television tubes, etc.

Exercise 1.13   *Materials used in electrical engineering*

1. Prepare a list of 10 material items that are made from moulded plastic or PVC-u and are used in electrical work. As an example, number one has been completed.

1	PVC-u conduit
2	
3	
4	
5	
6	
7	
8	
9	
10	

2. Where would you expect to find **carbon** used as an electrical component?

3. List five electrical accessories in your college that have been made from moulded plastic.

4. For this exercise you will have to get your tutor's permission to research areas of the college that would normally be out of bounds to you. Such areas could include the electrical mains distribution room, the central heating boiler house or the estate workshop area.

   Demonstrate to your assessor by natural observation within the workplace that you can identify and record a minimum of 10 materials used in electrical installation engineering. Use the space provided for your answer.

Material	Component/accessory	Use/application	Location
1. Aluminum			
2. Brass			
3. Carbon			
4. Ceramics			
5. Copper			
6. Glass			
7. Lead			
8. Magnesium oxide			
9. Malleable cast iron			
10. Mercury			
11. Moulded plastics			
12. Perspex®			
13. Polyvinylchoride (PVC)			
14. Steel and stainless steel			
15. Sulphuric acid			
16. Tungsten			

Once you have found a listed material, briefly describe the electrical component, accessory or appliance and where it may be inspected.

The IEE *Wiring Regulations*

The **Institution of Electrical Engineers's** (IEE) publication, *Wiring Regulations*, was accepted as a **British Standard** in 1992 and is known as BS 7671. It can studied in your college, or the public library will hold a copy. It can be bought from:

- large bookshops
- direct from the IEE
- most major electrical wholesalers.

Useful guides

The *Wiring Regulations* has been sub-divided into parts and sections. A section that would be of interest to the trainee engineer is the alphabetical list of **definitions** found at the front of the book. Here technical jargon is translated into everyday English. For example:

Appliance   'An item of current-using equipment other than a luminaire or an independent motor'

Insulation   'Suitable non-conductive material enclosing, surrounding or supporting a conductor'

Other than the index, the book is divided into Parts, Chapters, Tables and Sections. As an example:

Part 4 – Protection for safety
Chapter 41 – Protection against electric shock

Examples of the Wiring Regulations

Regulation 601–02–01:   No electrical equipment shall be installed in the interior of a bath tub or shower basin.

Regulation 527–01–02:   The wiring shall be installed so that the general structure of the building is not affected and fire safety is not put at risk.

To interpret, read your chosen paragraph a couple of times to try to understand its meaning – but if still in doubt, ask!

The *On Site Guide*

The IEE have published a small booklet called the *On Site Guide*, which sets out everyday regulations in a simple way. Only selected regulations are explained but it is well worth obtaining a copy. The *On Site Guide* is for qualified electricians and covers the following installations:

- Domestic installations
- Off-peak supplies (for example, night storage heating)
- Supplies to outhouses and garages
- Commercial installations (single and three-phase)
- Industrial installations (single and three-phase)
- Earthing arrangements

The *Guide* contains information required for general electrical installation work and greatly reduces the need for detailed calculations.

Exercise 1.14

The Wiring Regulations

For this exercise you will have to obtain a current edition of the IEE *Wiring Regulations*

1. The main equipotential bonding conductor must be clamped to unconnected parts, such as water and gas service intake pipes, which will conduct electricity. Which other unconnected electrically conductive parts should also be included? See Regulation 413–02–02.

2. Where would the main bonding conductor be connected at the electrical distribution board/centre?

3. Regulation 463–01–04 has been written with safety in mind. Rewrite the regulation using your own words.

4. Using your own words explain the meaning of the term 'supplementary insulation' as found in the IEE *Wiring Regulation's* List of Definitions.

5. Look through the *Wiring Regulations* and find out which Part, Chapter, or Section numbers are reserved for the following titles:

   (a) Protection for Safety – Part number:

   (b) Supplies for Safety Services – Chapter number:

   (c) Locations containing a bath tub or shower basin – Section:

   (d) Applications of Protective Measures for Safety – Chapter number:

   (e) Scope, Object and Fundamental Requirements for Safety – Part number:

6. Look up Regulation 601–07–07 and in your own words, using knowledge gained from this course, describe how a wiring system could be installed in order to satisfy this Wiring Regulation.

Graphical symbols used in electrical work

Simple graphical symbols have been designed to explain or record details of electrical/electronic wiring. British Standards and the **International Electrotechnical Commission** have published a European standard where each symbol is easily recognised. With familiarity, the symbols become much easier to remember.

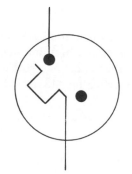

BS 3939 graphical symbol for a fluorescent light starter switch.

Creating your own symbols

When an installation is being designed always use the proper symbols and logos. Creating your own can be very confusing for everyone else; see Regulation 514–09–01.

Drawing a circuit

Follow these simple guide-lines:

- Draw all symbols the same size.

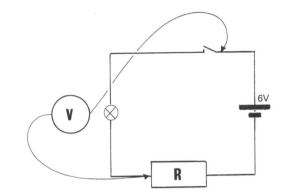

Avoid drawing different sized graphical symbols when options are available.

- Conductors are drawn as straight lines; vertically or horizontally.
- Avoid drawing diagonal lines.
- Use dotted lines to link components which act together, such as a double pole switch.

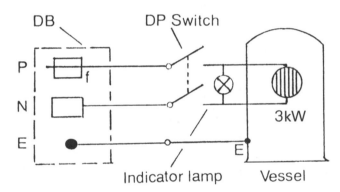

Components that operate together should be connected with a dotted line.

- When a wiring arrangement has both a cause and an effect, for example switching on a light, place the cause to the left and the effect to the right. If this is not possible it may be drawn from the top to the bottom.

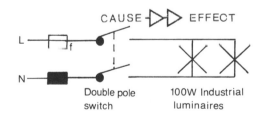

When a wiring diagram has a clear cause and effect,
the cause will be drawn to the left and the effect to the right.

Graphical symbols to BS 3939

The table on the following page lists graphical symbols from the International Electrotechnical Commission and British Standard 3939.

Name of component/accessory	Graphical symbol
Main control (distribution centre)	
Wall-mounted lighting point	
Heating element	
Thermostat	
Voltmeter	
Ammeter	
Resistor	
Horn	
Floodlight	
Time switch	
Alternating current (AC) relay	
Electric motor (general symbol)	
One-way switch (general symbol)	
Wiring (general symbol)	
Battery	
Indicator lamp	

| Exercise 1.15 | *Electrical location symbols* |

1. Why should you not make up your own graphical symbols when designing an electrical installation?

2. The figure below illustrates electrical components wired in a **cause and effect** fashion. Use BS 3939 electrical location symbols to draw a diagram of the circuit.

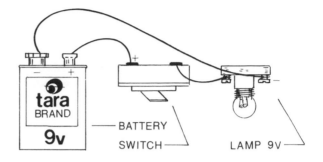

3. Design your own circuit using knowledge obtained from this course. Draw a wiring diagram using BS 3939 graphical symbols to include the following components:

   • A distribution fuseboard
   • A single pole (switching the live conductor) switch
   • A heating element

4. From knowledge gained, transfer the BS 3939 wiring diagram on page 67 into a picture to represent the physical layout of the circuit and components used.

(a) Label each component.
(b) Sketch in single wires to serve the components.
(c) Where possible show the point of termination.

Block diagrams

Block diagrams are a useful way to introduce an idea without the need for technical detail. Problem areas can be identified and sorted out, making it easier to plan ahead.

A block diagram for a direct current power supply can be built up as shown here.

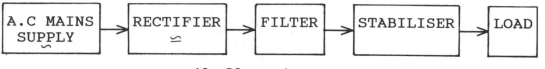

AC to DC conversion process

| Exercise 1.16 | *Block diagrams* |

1. List one reason why block diagrams can be useful during the development stages of a project.

2. Using a block diagram demonstrate the technique of lifting a heavy load. Research your college or workplace for 'lifting heavy loads' posters.

Cables and components used in electrical work

The following table gives information about a small selection of cables and components used in electrical installation engineering.

Item	Size/value	Use
Distribution centres	Variable up to 100 amp	Control and distribution of circuits
Flexible insulated cable	From 0.5 to 2.5 mm^2 (2–5 cores)	Accessories
PVC-insulated and sheathed cable	From 1 to 35 mm^2	Power and lighting, domestic and commercial installations
Steel and PVCu conduit	16, 20, 25, and 32 mm diameter	Cable carriers; used in industry
Conduit fittings steel and PVCu	16, 20, 25 and 32 mm diameter	Used in conjunction with conduct as cable draw-in and inspection boxes

Metric sized conduit fittings.
(Reproduced by kind permission of Walsal Conduits Ltd.)

Item	Size/value	Use
Switches, plugs, sockets, lampholders, etc.	Current rating between 2 and 32 amp	Wiring accessories
FP 200® fire resistant cable	Various sizes from 1 to 4 mm^2, obtainable in various cores	Fire alarm and detection circuits
Armoured PVC-insulated cables	Various sizes from 1.5 to 35 mm^2	Workshops, factories, industrial and commercial use

Steel wire armoured, PVC-insulated cable.
(Reproduced by kind permission of Walsal Conduits Ltd.)

Item	Size/value	Use
Trunking and cable tray	Various sizes, trunking; 50 × 50 mm to 300 × 150 mm cable tray: 50–900 mm in width	Industrial and commercial use, various PVCu trunking systems for domestic use

Steel cable-trunking (left) and cable tray (right) are used for electrical installations.
(Reproduced by kind permission of Walsal Conduits Ltd.)

Residual current device (RCD)	From 10 to 1000 milliamps at various load ratings	Circuit/installation protection against earth leakage voltages
Passive infra-red sensor	Will accept loads up to 13 amps	Automatic switching for lighting arrangements; used in intruder alarm installations
Mineral insulated cable (MI)	Various sizes and numbers of cores, from 1.0 mm² to 240 mm²	Hot environments and high-risk areas; used also in fire detection and alarm circuits

Mineral insulated cable (MI).

Telephone wire	Usually four pairs of two conductors, for low voltage and current use	Telephones and door entry systems, etc.
Bell wire	Flat twin and single insulated, usually about 0.75 mm²	For use with low voltage bell systems, low current rating

Exercise 1.17 *Cables and components*

1. An additional lathe has to be wired in an industrial workshop. Recommend a method of providing a supply to the lathe from information obtainable from the table above.

2. For this exercise you will require freedom of movement in your college.

   (a) Seek out, identify and list five of the following cables and components used in electrical engineering:

   • Steel conduit   Size: Location:

   • PVCu conduit   Size: Location:

- Twin 13 amp socket outlet   Make: Location:
- Electrical distribution centre   Type: Location:
- Trunking (steel or PVCu)   Size: Location:
- Cable tray (steel or PVCu)   Size: Location:
- Mineral insulated cable   –   Location:
- Armoured PVC-insulated cable   –   Location:
- Conduit fittings (steel or PVCu)   Type: Location:
- PVC-insulated and sheathed cable   –   Location:

Making and distributing electricity

A list of basic facts follows in summary form:

1. Alternating current (AC) was not in general use until 1890.
2. Examples of 'energy providers', which rotate giant machines called **alternators**, to generate electricity are:

   - Coal
   - Gas
   - Water (by means of dams)
   - Oil
   - Wave motion (experimental)
   - Wind

3. Electricity is generated at the power station between **11 000** and **33 000** volts AC. It is then increased in value by a process known as **transforming** to **132 000, 275 000** or **400 000** volts.

A typical electricity pylon serving the National Grid.

4. Sub-stations provide the means by which power taken from the **National Grid** can be reduced to 11 000 volts again. The reduced voltage is then routed across the countryside on wooden 'T' poles to local community transformers where it is further reduced to a familar 400/230 volts for industrial, commercial and domestic use.

Sub-stations such as this take power from the National Grid and reduce it to 11 000 volts.

Wooden poles distributing power to rural areas. This type of pole carries 11 000 volts.

Field transformer – reducing the voltage from 11 000 volts to 400/230 volts for industrial and domestic use.

5. Power stations are built away from towns and cities and are designed to blend in with the local surroundings.

Exercise 1.18

Power distribution: the National Grid

1. State whether the following statements are true or false in the spaces provided below.

   (a) Wave motion can be used to generate electricity.
   (b) The domestic voltage is 240 volts AC.
   (c) Power stations are usually built in cities and towns.
   (d) Sub-stations reduce the voltage taken from the National Grid to 400 and 230 volts AC.

   (a)   (b)   (c)   (d)

2. Draw a simple block diagram to explain the steps taken from power generation to domestic use.

3. This exercise, based on observation, is designed to test your practical understanding of the distribution of power from the National Grid System to rural areas.

   (a) Seek out, identify and list in the spaces provided the following cable supports:

   • National Grid pylon. Located at:
   • Sub-station serving the *National Grid*. Located at:
   • Wooden 'T' or 'H' poles for the distribution of power across the countryside.
       Located at:
   • Straight wooden poles distributing voltages to homes and industry.
       Located at:

   (b) Observe from a distance. Do not enter private property.

Electrical supply systems and earthing arrangements

There are several different types of supply systems and earthing arrangements to be found throughout the country; however **Regulation 312–03–01** covers the following categories:

• TT
• TNS
• TN-CS
• TNC

TT systems

This system is found in the countryside and requires the consumer to provide a suitable means of earth leakage protection. (This is the term used when a voltage is present where it is not intended, for example, on the metal casement of a window or domestic heater.) Protection usually takes the form of a residual current device (RCD).

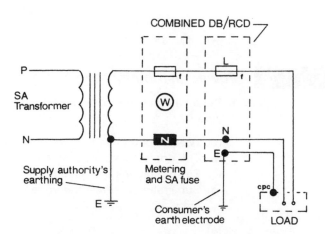

In a TT earthing arrangement the neutral conductor is connected to earth at the transformer and is completely independent of the consumer's earthing arrangement. DB = distribution board; RCD = residual current device (trip).

Only two conductors enter the dwelling: LIVE and NEUTRAL. The protective earth conductor or other means of protection has to be provided by the consumer.

TNS systems

This system is found in towns and cities where the lead sheath of the underground service cable acts as a protective conductor. The electrical installation is then earthed by connecting a conductor from the lead sheath of the service cable to an **earth terminal point**. A suitably sized conductor is then connected from the earth terminal point to the distribution centre as shown.

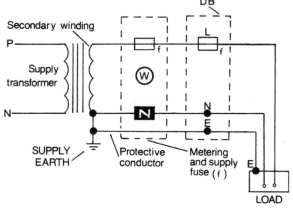

A TNS earthing arrangement.

TN-CS systems

A TN-CS system provides a combined **neutral** and **earth** conductor together with a **phase** conductor to serve an installation that has both separate and independent current protective and neutral conductors.

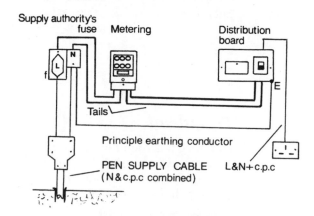

A typical TN-CS earthing arrangement shown in pictorial form.

The incoming combined neutral and earth **service conductor** is formed from the copper stranded armouring wrapped around the insulated live conductor. The copper armouring is also insulated with a layer of PVC. This system is designed for both rural and urban installations.

TNC systems

This type of system is rare. It is used with a privately owned **isolating transformer**, which is served with an **'input' voltage** from the local supply authority. Being an isolating transformer it will neither increase nor decrease the applied voltage, so the output voltage is the same as the input but it is physically separated from the public electricity supply.

All installation work (lighting and power) is carried out using **mineral insulated cables**, the copper sheath of the cable acting as a combined neutral and current protective conductor.

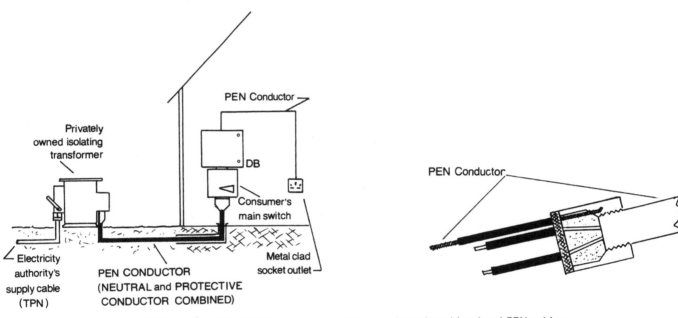

In a TNC system all installation work is carried out using mineral insulated PEN cables.
PEN = insulated phase conductor with a combined earth and neutral formed by the copper sheath.

Single and three phase supplies

A typical **single phase** 230 volt supply serving a private dwelling is shown here. The earthing arrangement is TNS.

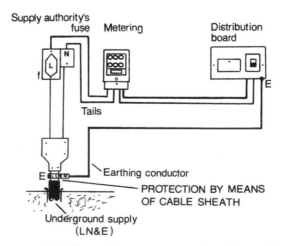

A single phase supply (TNS earthing arrangements) serving a private dwelling.

Single phase supplies are used to serve homes and small businesses where the demand for power is modest. Single phase supplies provide 230 volts AC and a current potential of between 60 and 100 amps.

Three phase supplies are designed to serve industry. A typical supply intake position where the earthing is TN-CS is shown here. The voltage supplied has a maximum value of 400 volts and a current potential from 100 amps upwards. This type of system is used to power large current-consuming machines and appliances, which are used in heavy and light engineering businesses.

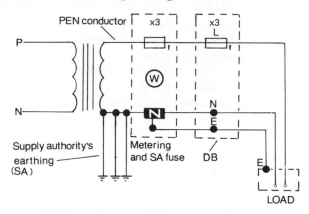

TN-CS earthing and metering arrangements.

Single phase voltage

- Between the phase conductor and neutral: 230 volts
- Between the phase conductor and earth of a TN-CS, TNC or TNS earthing arrangement: 230 volts

Three phase voltage

Measuring the voltage of a three-phase and neutral supply will show the following values:

- Between any combination of all three phases: 400 volts
- Between any phase and earth, apart from a TT system of earthing: 230 volts

Testing a TT system from the phase conductor to earth could produce a lower value than expected as the electricity has to return to the transformer through the soil.

Direct current supplies

Direct current supplies are now reserved for the following uses:

- Research establishments (AC current is changed to DC to provide an output of 220 volts; this is known as **rectification**)
- Hotels and shops (where central battery systems are used to serve emergency lighting arrangements)
- Factories and workshops using battery supplied emergency lighting
- Electronic workshops
- Large commercial workshops (where DC is supplied by individual industrial units)

Exercise 1.19

Electrical supply systems

1. Describe in the space below, using your own words, how an installation is provided with an earthing point when served with a TNS system of wiring.

2. Where might you find a 220 volt DC supply?

3. What is a customer asked to provide when supplied with a TT electrical arrangement?

4. This exercise is based on observation. The co-operation of your college estate office will be required.

(a) What type of earthing arrangement and supply voltage is serving your college?

(b) If the supply intake position is covered, ask your resident maintenance person to show you how an earth is provided to protect the installation.

(c) From information gained, record by writing in the space provided:

1. The voltage serving the college:

2. The earthing arrangement:

3. The location of the mains:

4. Date of observation:

5. Answer the following questions in the spaces provided.

(a) What is the supply voltage and earthing arrangement serving your home or the home of a friend?

(b) Observe how the service cable is terminated and how an earth, if any, is provided for the installation.

(c) With knowledge gained, draw a sketch of the electrical supply intake arrangement serving your home, in the space provided.

The type of earthing arrangement is:
The house is situated in the town/country (delete one)
Date of observation:

Circuit protection

The table below covers the types of circuit protection for use with simple AC and DC circuits.

Type of protection and application	Comments	Advantages	Disadvantages
Semi-enclosed (rewirable); low cost installations	Fuse elements obtainable in 5, 10, 15, 20 and 30 amp	Cheap; static; easy to see when ruptured; low cost when needed to replace	Wrong size fuse wire can be fitted; will deteriorate with age; can be fitted with a fault in circuit
Small cartridge fuse; for use with 13 amp plugs	Fuses are coloured and have their values printed on the side; maximum 13 amps	No moving parts; small; colour coded; accurate current rating	The printed current rating and colour can be rubbed off; can be replaced with the wrong fuse; can be shorted out when ruptured

Overcurrent protection devices. From left to right: miniature circuit breaker (MCB), moulded case circuit breaker (MCCB), cartridge fuse, plug fuse, and a semi-enclosed (rewirable).

Type of protection and application	Comments	Advantages	Disadvantages
High breaking capacity fuse; for use in motor circuits and sub-mains	A larger fuse than the cartridge fuse; fitted with an indicator bead, which disappears when the fuse has blown	Can see when the fuse is blown; very reliable	Very expensive; can be shorted out when the fuse element has blown
Miniature circuit breakers (MCB); general protection for domestic circuits; used in industrial and commercial installations	A switch-like device in various current ratings up to 63 amps; has moving parts	Rating cannot be altered; supply easily restored; overcurrent quickly identified	Expensive; have moving parts that can wear; affected by temperature
Moulded case circuit breaker (MCCB); can be used to protect main supply conductors; Various current ratings up to 800 amps	There are two types: 1. Magnetic 2. Thermal Physically larger than MCBs; has moving parts	Able to carry and handle far greater currents than MCBs	Very expensive

| Exercise 1.20 | *Overcurrent protection* |

1. State the most economical way to provide overcurrent protection.

2. List two overcurrent devices that have moving parts.

3. List two reasons why it would be better to fit a miniature circuit breaker as a means of overcurrent protection rather than a less expensive semi-enclosed fuse.

4. State in the space provided whether the following sentence is true or false:
High breaking capacity (HBC) fuses are both thermally and magnetically assisted.

5. For this exercise you will be given the following:

- A moulded case circuit breaker (MCCB)
- A miniature circuit breaker (MCB)
- A high breaking capacity fuse (HBC)
- A cartridge fuse
- A semi-enclosed fuse

(a) Demonstrate by observation and selection that you are able to recognise the overcurrent protection devices listed.
(b) Demonstrate to your assessor that you know how each overcurrent device is best applied.
(Bear in mind that design differences occur, depending on manufacture.)

6. Your assessor will show you a distribution centre that would be ideally suited for a domestic installation or used to serve a small commercial premise. Demonstrate to your assessor that you can identify the type of overcurrent protection used in the distribution centre.

Precautions taken when working with electricity

Safety in the workplace is often taken for granted by many apprentice engineers. This attitude could mean the difference between life and death, so everyone must make sure that they know the latest safety procedures and regulations covering their work.

Accidents involving electricity can be prevented by keeping alert and being aware of any possible dangers. Always think ahead, as you would when tackling an engineering problem and do not create a dangerous situation for yourself or anyone else.

A list follows, containing points to help safety when undertaking work applied to electrical engineering:

1. Find out who your factory/workshop first aid person is.
2. Obey safety rules, signs and warning notices.

BS 5378
Part 1

A selection of safety signs found in factories.

3. Never try to carry heavy or bulky electrical equipment of more than **20 kg** in weight without assistance.
4. Never tamper with electrical '**interlock**' switches serving machinery while the electricity is switched on.
5. Wear sensible protective clothing and a face mask when necessary.
6. Do not take risks involving **live conductive parts**. Wear good fitting electrical gloves.
7. Switch off workshop electrical equipment that is being worked on when practical to do so.
8. Keep your hands dry and free from workshop dirt, oil, etc., when carrying out electrical work.
9. Remove rings, watches and bracelets when work has to be carried out on live conductive parts. This will stop a **flash-over** occurring, which can happen if jewellery becomes caught up in electrical equipment.
10. Always read the instruction manual first.
11. Thoroughly check for damaged components and replace when necessary.
12. Avoid the use of power tools in the rain.
13. Fit a **residual current device** plug onto power extension leads intended for use outdoors. This will prevent lethal currents passing through the human body, should a fault condition occur, from the **phase** conductor to **earth.**
14. Inspect power leads for mechanical damage.
15. Use only 110 volt power tools when your work takes you to a construction site.
16. Handle charged capacitors with care. They are able to store a great deal of energy.
17. Use the correct type of protective clothing when working with **secondary cells** (batteries).

18. Dispose of spent lamps (lamps which no longer work) wisely. They contain many toxic materials.
19. Safely store all test instruments and keep them in their carrying cases. Damaged instruments may lead to faulty values being recorded.
20. Unwind extension power cables from the reel to prevent them warming up.
21. Take care when deciding where to place extension cables. Keep clear of workshop machinery and busy areas.
22. Do not smoke or use a naked flame in a room containing secondary cells that are being charged. There could be an explosive atmosphere.
23. Keep your workplace tidy and free from rubbish and litter. Electrical work can be carried out far more efficiently in areas free from obstacles, which could hinder progress or cause an accident.
24. Allow a **jigsaw** to stop before removing it from the workpiece; this will prevent the blade from shattering and causing possible injury.
25. Do not work alone on live workshop equipment. Immediate assistance can be offered should an accident happen.
26. Regularly inspect plugs serving hand-held workshop power tools for damaged, loose or disconnected conductors. When a 13 amp mains plug is used, check the size of fuse that has been installed.
27. Masonry nails serving cable clips can snap and fly causing injury when not hammered home squarely. Use suitable eye protection.
28. Using blunt tools for electrical work is dangerous. Keep screwdrivers well ground and handsaws sharp.
29. Read the **Electricity at Work Regulations**. There is probably a poster in your factory.
30. Never take risks – people are far more important than property!

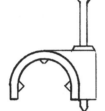

This type of cable clip is used to fix round-bodied flexible cable to surfaces.

Exercise 1.21

Precautions taken when using electrical equipment

1. What type of clothing/gear would you use when doing the following jobs? Answer in the spaces below.

   (a) Working with plastic cable clips served with hardened masonry nails
   (b) Secondary cell maintenance work
   (c) Working on live conductive parts at mains voltages

   (a)

   (b)

   (c)

2. Why is it sensible to store test instruments safely when not in use?

3. Research your college library to find the names of at least four toxic or dangerous substances found in modern lamps. Write in the space provided, which types of lamp contain toxic substances. One example has been given.

   1. Mercury (fluorescent lamps)

   2.

   3.

   4.

4. For this exercise you will need freedom of movement throughout your college. Locate, sketch and name six of any of the following that are found in your college:

   • Charts providing safety information
   • Posters summarising industrial regulations
   • Black and yellow safety warning signs

As an example the first has been completed for you.

Location	Sketch of sign or title of notice, etc.	Name/application
Electrical mains room		Electrical hazard

First aid procedures

First aid treatment is intended to provide treatment for minor injuries and to give first aid assistance until professional medical help arrives.

The following points are useful first aid tips for those working in the electrical engineering industry:

1. Injury to the eye must be treated by qualified medical staff. Failure to obtain treatment could lead to more serious damage.
2. Battery acid splashes on the skin must be thoroughly removed with clean water. Seek medical attention as soon as possible.
3. Cuts and scratches caused by electrical components must be thoroughly cleaned with fresh water. Apply antiseptic solution to the wound and press firmly using a small section of sterile bandage made into a small pad until the bleeding has stopped. A first aid plaster may then be applied to the wound.
4. Never apply a cotton wool dressing directly to a wound as this type of dressing will stick, making it difficult to remove.
5. Take care when using hand-held geared power tools. Always hold the machine firmly to avoid sprained or damaged wrists should the tool unexpectedly seize while working stubborn masonry.
6. Check, from time to time, the contents of your workshop or personal first aid box so that items which have been used may be replaced.
7. Never allow yourself to become careless when doing electrical work.

Coping with an emergency: mouth-to-mouth resuscitation techniques

If someone stops breathing after having been in direct contact with electricity, brain damage can occur within three minutes due to lack of oxygen. So it is very important to start **mouth-to-mouth resuscitation** as soon as possible after the accident. This technique must continue until the victim starts breathing normally again. Remember these five important points; it might help to save a colleague's life!

1. Switch off the supply of electricity.
2. If this is not practical, push the victim away from the source of current by using a wooden broom, a chair or a length of dry hosepipe. Do not use any material that might be damp such as a towel or workshop waste rag.
3. Never touch the victim with your hands until he or she has been removed from live electrical parts, or you could become another victim.
4. Ask someone to call for your factory first-aider.
5. When breathing has stopped the following procedure must be carried out:

   (a) Lay the casualty on his or her back.
   (b) With head placed to one side, clear any obstructions from the victim's mouth to avoid choking.

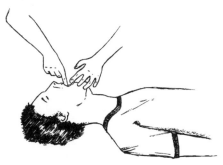

Place the victim's head to one side and remove any material from the mouth.

   (c) Next, tilt his or her head fully backwards by placing one hand on the forehead and the other on the neck.

To open the air passage, tilt the casualty's head fully backwards.

   (d) Check that the pulse is present at the neck. (The large artery at the neck is known as the **carotid artery**.)
   (e) Transfer your hand from the neck and tilt the victim's chin upwards.

(f) Pinch the victim's nostrils together using your fingers. Then take a deep breath and blow into the casualty's mouth as shown here. Repeat!

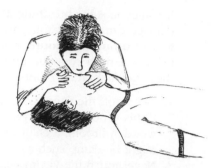

Pinch the casualty's nose and blow two rapid
breaths into his or her mouth.

(g) Check to see that the chest responds by rising and falling after each ventilation. If this does not happen, tilt the head well back and blow through the victim's nose, closing his or her mouth with your hand.

(h) Continue ventilations at the normal breathing rate.

(i) When breathing has started and is considered normal, recheck the casualty's neck pulse and place him or her in the recovery position as illustrated.

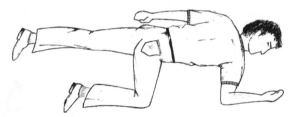

Place the casualty in the recovery position
once breathing has started properly.

(j) Contact your medical centre without delay.

(k) Make sure that either you or someone else stays with the victim until professional help arrives.

Exercise 1.22 | *First aid procedures*

1. Why must you never touch a victim of direct contact with electricity, using your bare hands?

2. Why should you remove obstructions such as false teeth, chewing gum, confectionery, tobacco products, etc., from your patient's mouth?

3. Why should you never apply a cotton wool dressing directly to an open wound?

4. Where is the carotid artery to be found?

5. For this exercise you will need a medical mannequin.

(a) Demonstrate to your assessor that you have a basic 'hands-on' knowledge of mouth-to-mouth resuscitation techniques using a medical mannequin doll.

(b) First assume that your patient is lying against a live conductive part. Demonstrate how you would remove the victim from the source of power without causing injury to yourself.

(c) Talk your way through the procedure during mouth-to-mouth resuscitation explaining why certain routines have to be carried out.

(d) Assume after your resuscitation demonstration that your patient has started to breath normally again. Demonstrate to your assessor that you know the routine which has to follow once breathing has started again.

Measuring voltages and currents safely

Earlier in this chapter, we learnt how voltage can be measured by placing voltmeter probes in parallel with the circuit to be tested.

Current flowing in a circuit is measured with an ammeter, or a workshop multimeter, placed in series formation with the circuit.

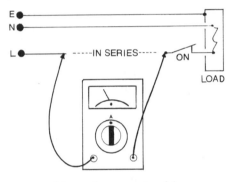

Measuring current safely.

Using your meter safely

Remember the following points:

1. Is there enough insulation on the test probes?
2. Have the meter and probes been checked for damage?
3. Has each probe '**finger barriers**' to guard against accidental hand contact with live conductive parts?
4. Is there good all round insulation apart from a maximum of 2 mm exposed metal forming the probe tip?
5. Are the leads coloured so that one can be identified from the other?
6. Are the leads flexible?
7. Are the service leads from the probes a suitable length – ideally 1.2 metres?
8. If the leads come away from the insulated probes, will the person who is testing be safe from exposed conductive parts?
9. Is there a built-in service fuse inside the body of the probe?
10. Has the instrument been switched to the correct setting before testing starts?

If you have answered YES to all 10 points, the demands of **Guidance Note GS 38** from the **Health and Safety Executive** have been fulfilled.

GS 38 safety probes

A typical GS 38 probe and its lead would have the following specifications:

- A probe of about 220 mm in length
- Coloured probes and cable insulation (one red and one black in the United Kingdom)
- Doubly insulated supporting a multi-stranded conductor with a cross-sectional area of 1.5 mm²
- Probe/cable insulation value of 600 volts AC/DC

- Fitted with a BS 88/Part 1 HRC fuse rated at 500 milliamps
- Moulded finger guards and finger and thumb grips
- Retractable metal probe tips

A typical GS 38 instrument probe with associated leads.
(Reproduced by kind permission of Robin Electronics Ltd.)

Precautions taken

Engineers must take suitable precautions against the risk from electric shock and burns whenever using test instruments on live conductive parts.

Problems which can occur are:

- Burns and flash-overs caused by the use of badly made test probes
- Arcing caused by too much current
- The selector switch not being set correctly. Live voltages must not be applied to the test probes when the test meter has been set to record **resistance** as the meter may be damaged.

Exercise 1.23

Using test instruments safely

1. Explain, using your own words, why engineers testing live circuits should take suitable precautions.

2. What could be the result of using poorly insulated test probes when measuring high voltage?

3. For this exercise you will require the following:

   - A multimeter with AC/DC facilities
   - A 24 volt AC or DC supply
   - Insulated wire (0.5 mm²)
   - A single pole switch
   - Two mechanical wire connectors
   - A small terminal screwdriver
   - A 22 ohm wire wound resistor rated at 50 watts ±5%

   Demonstrate to your assessor that you can measure voltages up to 24 volts, current up to 2 amps and resistance in circuit using a battery or other low voltage supply.

   (a) Demonstrate that you can use a multimeter test instrument both correctly and safely. An accuracy of 5% will be expected when using an analogue meter or 1% if a digital meter is used.

(b) Select a suitable test instrument and check the ohms scale for accuracy.

(c) Connect the resistor, switch and power supply as shown. Use your knowledge of BS 3939 location symbols to interpret the meaning of the wiring arrangement.

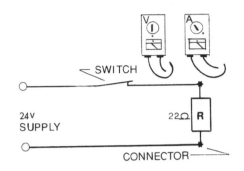

(d) When you have completed the circuit, switch ON and measure the voltage across the 22 ohm resistor. Log the value in the space provided.

(e) Switch OFF and place the test instrument in circuit in order to measure the value of current flow. Observe the correct polarity if a DC supply is used.

(f) Switch the circuit back ON and note the value in amps drawn from the circuit. Write the value in the space provided.

(g) Calculate by the use of Ohm's Law the **power** developed in **watts** and write the value in the space provided.

(h) Remembering past learning, measure the value of the load resistor in ohms with your test instrument. Is the value obtained any different from the manufacturer's declared value of 22 ohms? Write the value and any differential in the space provided.

Voltage value:

Value of current in amps:

Value of power in watts:

Value of the resistor in ohms:

Difference in value between the declared value of 22 ohms and the value obtained:

Chapter 2
Basic electrical wiring

All information presented in this section is complete, accurate and legible	
All information presented in this section is in the format required	
The trainee observes statutory regulations at all times	
The trainee implements safe operating practice and always demonstrates regard for the safety of others	

The Health and Safety at Work Act: cables and wires

Cables must always be handled correctly and safely so there is no health risk to the user. A list of helpful safety points follows:

1. Cables must be installed by a competent person in accordance with the **Wiring Regulations** and **Codes of Practice**.
2. Cuts and scratches to the hands can be caused when mineral insulated cable is terminated without care.
3. The **magnesium oxide** insulation serving mineral insulated cables can cause irritation if any particles enter the eyes. It can also have a slightly drying effect on the skin.

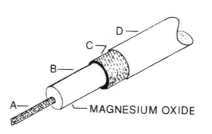

The white powdered insulation serving mineral insulated cables can cause irritation if enters the eyes. A = conductor; B = insulation; C = copper sheath; D = PVC sheath.

4. Large heavy cable drums and some types of cable packaging can have sharp metal components, which could cause problems when handling.
5. If large amounts of powdered magnesium oxide insulation are accidentally swallowed, diarrhoea could result.
6. Burning cable insulation in the open is illegal (see The Clean Air Act 1956). Toxic fumes are produced.
7. Cables should not be high-temperature heated, welded or melted if certain health risks are to be avoided.
8. Steel binding straps are often used for packaging large cables. These straps must be cut carefully so they do not unexpectedly spring out.
9. The Safety at Work Act states that appropriate information for the correct handling and proper use of cables is made available to the user.
10. Cable dispensed from a large wooden drum should be handled using a pair of **cable jacks** and a solid circular steel bar. The cable should always be drawn from the top and the drum must never be left unattended and free to rotate.
11. Cable should only be used for its intended purpose. If a cable with a smaller than required current rating is used, overheating will occur.

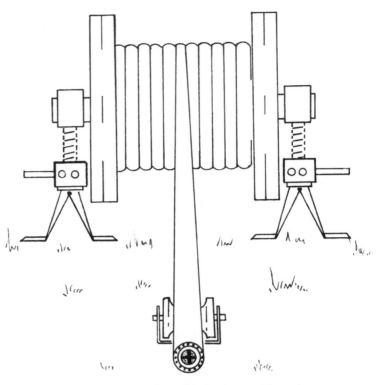

Use cable jacks and a solid circular steel bar when
cable is removed from a large wooden drum.

The *Wiring Regulations*: cables and wires

There are many regulations covering the safe use of cables but space will allow
only a small selection of them to be reviewed. The numbered paragraphs below are
paraphrased from the *Wiring Regulations* to enable easier reading.

1. There are three types of circuits used in electrical installation engineering and these
   are known as **Category 1**, **Category 2**, and **Category 3** circuits. Each category of
   circuit must be segregated by **mechanical means** or by **distance** from the others.
   Category 1 circuit: A circuit operating at a voltage not exceeding 1000 volts
   AC or 1500 volts DC between conductors and supplied directly from the mains.
   Category 2 circuit: A circuit used for telecommunications, sound distribution,
   intruder alarms, radio, bell-call systems and data transmission circuits that originate
   from a safety source.
   Category 3 circuits: A fire alarm or emergency lighting circuit.
2. Reference is made to Regulation 523–05–01. The metallic sheaths of armoured
   single core cables must be bonded together at both ends of their run. Alternatively,
   the armoured sheath of cables with conductors, of more than 50 mm^2, and a plastic
   or insulated outer sheath may be bonded together at one point.
3. The neutral conductor in a circuit, which has **discharge lighting**, must not be
   less in size than the phase conductor. Discharge lighting is lighting in which an
   electrical discharge takes place in a vacuum or in a gaseous atmosphere. See
   Regulation 524–02–03.
4. Wiring Regulation 527–01–02 states that electrical wiring must not interfere with
   the structral performance and fire safety of a building.
5. An extra low voltage circuit of not more than 50 volts AC or 120 volts DC between
   conductors must be physically separated from low voltage mains, which are not
   more than 1000 volts AC or 1500 volts DC. See Regulation 528–01–02.
6. Aluminium or copper-clad aluminium conductors must not be used for
   underground connections to an earth electrode. See Regulation 547–03–02.

7. Surface wiring installations serving bathrooms must be free from steel conduit and trunking systems, bare metalic cable sheaths and uninsulated bonding conductors. See Regulation 601–07–01.

8. Agricultural wiring systems must be completely inaccessible to livestock. See Regulation 605–12–01.

Copies of the current edition of the IEE *Wiring Regulations* may be found in your college library or the Reference Section of most leading public libraries. Alternatively copies can be bought directly from the IEE.

Exercise 2.1

Cables and wires: Wiring Regulations *and health and safety*

1. What will happen if the current rating of a cable is too small for its intended purpose? Give your answer in the space below.

2. What would happen if particles of the insulation serving mineral insulated cable enters the eye?

3. For this practical exercise you will require the use of the current edition of the *Wiring Regulations*.

   (a) Demonstrate to your assessor that you are able to find the regulation governing the scope of Category 1, 2 and 3 circuits.
   (b) Where else in the regulations book can you obtain this information?
   (c) Write your answers in the space provided.

   Wiring Regulations number:

   Also obtainable from:

4. For this exercise you will need to retain your copy of the *Wiring Regulations*. Regulation 543–03 deals with electrical continuity conductors. It states that a protective conductor must be suitably protected against certain factors. What are these factors? Write your answer in the space provided.

   A protective conductor shall be suitably protected against the following:

5. For this exercise you will need to borrow or obtain an up-to-date '**product manual**' in which cables and wires are catalogued.

   (a) Find a section in the cable catologue in which **Section 6** of the *Health and Safety at Work Act* is reviewed.
   (b) Read thoroughly and write down what you consider to be the most important safety/health statement relating to cables and wires.

   The most important safety/health statement relating to cables and wires is:

Types of cable and their uses

There are many types of cable; each having their own particular role to play in electrical engineering. The following table lists six common types used in the industry today.

Cable	Typical insulation	Application
Single wire cables	PVC	Fixed power and lighting installations drawn into conduit or cable trunking systems; smaller cables of this type are used in the electronics industry
Multi-stranded single wire cables	PVC	Used for fixed power and lighting installations where the installation is subjected to flexing; often used in agricultural and horicultural situations
Co-axial	Outer sheath PVC; inner dielectric made from polyethylene or polyterafluorethylene	Single wire conductor or stranded where the cable is subjected to flexing; the screening may be made from bare, tinned or silver-plated copper; used in high frequency electronics, data transmission and television Co-axial cable. A = conductor/signal wire; B = polyethylene dielectric; C = screen; D = outer sheath.
Screened	PVC	Used for signal transmission, machine tool circuits, computer and regulating equipment; often applied to control circuits, presses and vehicle hoisting equipment
Flexible	PVC or PVC and acryle nitrite buthadience rubber	Used in portable and mobile equipment, domestic and commercial appliances and as flexible control cable; it may also be used as pendant drops serving lampholders in domestic installations and to serve inspection hand-lamps and extension leads
PVC-insulated and sheathed cable	PVC sheath PVC cable insulation	Used for fixed wiring purposes to serve wiring accessories in domestic, and small commercial installations; most houses are wired using this type of cable PVC-insulated and sheathed cable. A = conductor; B = insulation; C = protective conductor (earth); D = outer sheath.

How a cable is constructed

A typical armoured, PVC-insulated cable is constructed as shown here. The plastic shroud is designed to protect the brass cable gland.

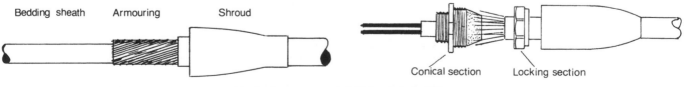

Bedding sheath   Armouring   Shroud

Conical section   Locking section

Steel wire armoured, PVC-insulated cable.

| Exercise 2.2 | *Cables and their uses* |

This exercise will test your practical understanding of cables. You will be given four commonly used cables, which are number referenced.

(a) Demonstrate to your assessor that you can correctly identify each cable.
(b) Discuss with your assessor the role each cable would play in electrical/electronic engineering.
(c) Write in the space provided the type of cable reviewed and how it may be applied.

Choosing the right cable

It is extremely important to select the most suitable cable for each particular electrical wiring task. There are many factors to be considered and a list of these follows:

- Situation (industrial, commercial, domestic, agricultural, etc.)
- Environment (inside, outside, above ground, below ground, etc.)
- Fauna (cattle, rodents, domestic animals, etc.)
- Flora (plants, shrubs, trees, bushes, root formations, etc.)
- Temperature (extreme heat or cold, moderate conditions)
- Applied voltage (extra low, low or high)
- Design current (milliamps, amps or kiloamps)
- Use (bell circuit, motor circuit, data transmission circuit, aerial leads, dwellings, shops and factories, etc.)
- The wetness factor (dry, humid, moist, saturated and submerged, etc.)
- Underground (extra low, low or high voltages, etc.)
- Explosive situations (chemical, fuel oil, coal, gas, battery charging rooms, grain silos, etc.)

Practical examples

1. Mineral insulated cables (MI) may be used with confidence for the following uses:

   - Areas of extreme heat, emergency lighting arrangements, fire detection and alarm systems
   - Corrosive, radioactive atmospheres and in areas where the cable could be subjected to knocks through carelessness

2. PVC-insulated and sheathed cables may be used for:

   - Low-risk domestic or commercial installations
   - Lighting and power requirements in schools and colleges

3. Wire armour, PVC-insulated and sheathed cables (SWA cable) may be used for:

   - Underground distribution systems
   - Industrial uses and control circuits

Selecting the size of cable

There are many points to be considered when deciding which size of cable to use in a circuit. In summary these are:

1. The surrounding temperature
2. Bunching (the term used when cables are grouped together)
3. Design current (the value of the current in amps expected to flow in the circuit)
4. Installation method (enclosed in conduit, clipped to a surface enclosed in cable trunking, embedded in plaster, fixed to catenary wiring, single core cable suspended free in air)
5. The rating of the protective device, i.e. the fuse of circuit breaker (this value in amps that the device can carry)
6. Voltage drop (on very large runs of cable the voltage drop would be noticeable if the design current is high)
7. **Correction factors** have been introduced to allow calculations to be made to determine the correct cable rating size for an installation. The four categories of correction factors to be taken into consideration are:

    C_g **Cable grouping** factor (when cables are grouped or bunched together)
    C_a Factor used for ambient or **surrounding temperature**
    C_i Factor used when the cable is placed inside or is in contact with **thermal insulation**

    - If only one side of the cable is in contact, the correction factor = 0.75
    - If the cable is surrounded by thermal insulation, the correction factor = 0.5

    C_f A factor of 0.725 is used when the protective device is a **semi-enclosed fuse** (often known as a rewirable fuse). This factor is not applied when the installation is to be carried out using mineral insulated cable.

A practical example: a circuit served by a semi-enclosed fuse

The following case is given as a practical example.

Problem:

A 230 volt, 3000 watt factory space heater wired using single PVC-insulated copper conductors, is protected by a 15 amp semi-enclosed fuse. The installation is to be carried out in an area where the maximum ambient temperature is 35°C. The circuit will be grouped and placed inside a steel conduit accompanied by two other single phase circuits. Each circuit will have identical loads to the proposed space heater circuit as illustrated here.

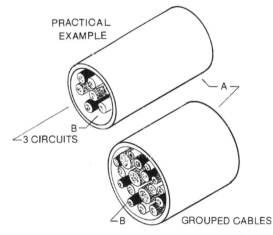

Grouped cables placed in a steel conduit; installation method
three of the *Wiring Regulations*. A = steel conduit; B = grouped cables.

Determine the minimum size conductor which may be used so as comply with the *Wiring Regulations*.

Solution:

A step-by-step approach follows:

1. Work out the value of the design current (I_B) of the circuit. This can be either equal to or slightly more than the current rating of the proposed protective device (I_n).

$$I_B = \frac{3000 \text{ watts}}{230 \text{ volts}}$$

I_B (the design current) = 13 amps

2. Next find the correction factor for an **ambient temperature** of 35°C (C_a). Regulation Table 4C1 will provide a factor of 0.94.
3. Now determine the **grouping factor** for single core PVC-insulated copper cable enclosed in conduit (C_g). Regulation Table 4B1 provides a factor of 0.70.
4. Finally, apply the correction factor for a **semi-enclosed BS 3036 fuse** (C_f) which is 0.725.

   As there is no thermal insulation to consider, correction factor C_i does not apply to this calculation.

   Work out the value of the minimum current carrying capacity of the cable to be used for the circuit. This is known as I_z.

$$I_z = \frac{\text{Rating of the protective device in amps}}{\text{Temperature factor} \times \text{grouping factor} \times \text{fuse factor}}$$

or, as an expression

$$I_z = \frac{I_n}{C_a \times C_g \times C_f}$$

Substituting for known values

$$I_z = \frac{15}{0.94 \times 0.7 \times 0.725}$$

$$I_z = \frac{15}{0.477}$$

$$I_z = 31.4 \text{ amps.}$$

This represents the minimum current carrying capacity of the cable (I_z).

5. A cable can now be selected from Table 4A of the *Wiring Regulations* under Installation Method 3. This will show that a 4 mm² (in cross-sectional area) conductor with a current carrying capacity of 32 amps would be the correct size to use. See Table 4D1A in the *Wiring Regulations*.

Volt drop

It is important to consider volt drop when a calculation is made to decide which size of conductor to use. Regulation 525-01-02 states that voltage drop between the incoming supply terminals and a fixed current consuming appliance (e.g. cooker, fan, radio, space heater, etc.) should not not be more than 4% of the **nominal voltage** (U_o) of the supply. The nominal voltage is the expected or the declared voltage of the supply.

Volt drop may be calculated using the following expression:

$$\text{Permissible volt drop} = U_o \times 0.04$$

where U_o is the nominal voltage of the supply and 0.04 is the percentage volt drop permitted.

The *Wiring Regulations* show a selection of values of voltage drop in the form of simple, easy-to-read tables.

| Exercise 2.3 | *Thermal insulation and volt drop* |

1. A 230 volt, 1000 watt electric space heater is to be wired using PVC-insulated and sheathed copper cable and will be protected by a 5 amp semi-enclosed fuse to BS 3036 (I_n). The cable will be totally surrounded by thermal insulation but will be laid apart from others. The temperature throughout the route will rise to a maximum of 35°C.

   Calculate the minimum current rating of the cable to serve the proposed installation, (I_z), given that:

(a) A factor of 0.5 will apply when a cable is totally surrounded by thermal insulation.

(b) A factor of 0.725 will apply when a semi-enclosed fuse is used as protection.

(c) A factor of 0.94 will apply when the ambient temperature is 35°C.

2. For the purpose of this practical exercise your tutor will measure and provide the nominal voltage of your supply under load conditions.

(a) Demonstrate to your assessor that you are able to determine whether the voltage value provided is acceptable and falls within the demands of the *Wiring Regulations*.

(b) Record your results and comments in the space provided.

Voltage value provided	Nominal value of the supply	Percentage under/over	Comments

3. Permission will be required for a supervised visit to your central heating/control room.

(a) Write down in the space provided the types of cables found.

(b) Are the cables provided suitable for the environment and the equipment they serve?

Type of cable	Temperature of the central heating room (hot, cold, cool)	Comments/observations, suitability of the cable

Materials used for conductors

There are many materials used as electrical conductors. The table below shows a few used in electrical installation engineering. Great care must be taken to avoid shearing the wire when brass terminal screws are used to terminate small aluminium conductors. Compared with copper, aluminium is very soft and will snap easily.

Electrical conductor	Application
Gold, silver and platinum	Electrical contacts and some electronic components
Copper	Cable, switching contacts, wires, earth rods, bus-bars and electric motor field coils, etc.
Aluminium	Overhead power cables serving the National Grid system. Fixed wiring cables in lieu of copper. Phase-earth/neutral (PEN) cables supplying dwellings. Cable sheathing
Lead	Lead plates for accumulators, filament lamp end-caps, cable sheathing Lead is used for connection pads at the bottom of filament lamps.

Electrical conductor	Application
Mercury	Tilt switches, rectifiers which convert alternating current (AC) to direct current (DC) and mercury cells (voltage = 1.35 V)
Brass (an alloy consisting of copper and zinc)	Nuts, bolts and washers used at points of electrical connection, lampholders connected to an electrical earth and terminal screws
Tungsten	Lamp filaments

Electrical insulating materials

The table below provides an insight into the many different insulating materials that are used in electrical engineering work.

Insulating material	Application
Polyvinyl chloride (PVC)	Cable insulation and sheathing. PVCu is moulded to form conduit and electrical accessories.
Synthetic rubber (neoprene, nitrile rubber and silicones)	Used as cable insulation or sleeving. Will withstand thermal and mechanical shock. Often used to serve immersion heater elements.
Polythene	Used as insulation for airfield lighting cables. Also used in some television aerial cables.
Magnesium oxide (magnesia)	Used as an insulator for mineral insulated cables (MI). Very high melting point. Used also in some types of semi-conductors. Magnesia is used as an insulator for mineral insulated cables. (Reproduced by kind permission of Walsal Conduits Ltd.)
90°C thermosetting	This type of insulation is soft when cool but changes to a hard and rigid form upon heating. Used in fire resistant cables.
Cross-linked polyethylene (XLPE)	Power distribution cables and when cables are required to be buried. Temperature range: −40°C to +90°C.
Natural rubber	Used as insulation and sheathing for special cables. Once used for fixed wiring applications.
Bakelite®	Not often use for electrical insulation purposes but may still be found serving older toggle type switches serving lighting circuits.
Ceramic	Fuse element holders and the bases of lighting switches, etc.

Colour codes used for conductors

Flexible conductors

- Twin flexible cable: brown (phase), blue (neutral)
- Three-core flexible cable: brown (phase), blue (neutral) and green/yellow (current protective conductor)
- Four-core flexible cable: brown, black, blue and green/yellow (current protective conductor)
- Five-core flexible cable: black, blue, brown, black and green/yellow (current protective conductor). Note that there are two black conductors serving this flexible cable.

Non-flexible conductors (multi-core)

The two principal types of non-flexible cable, stranded and solid conductors, are colour-coded indentically.

- Two-core: red (phase), black (neutral)
- Three-core: red, yellow and blue
- Four-core: red, yellow, blue and black (usually the first colours are reserved for phases L1, L2 and L3, whilst the black conductor is used as a neutral)
- Five-core and above: white insulation with black numbers

Single-core non-sheathed conductors

These cables are served with toughened copper conductors and are PVC-insulated. The standard colours are:

- Red
- White
- Yellow
- Blue
- Brown
- Black
- Grey
- Green/yellow

Black coloured cable is reserved for the **neutral** conductor while the **current protective conductor** is green/yellow. Red, yellow and blue coloured conductors are usually used for **three-phase** installations or two-way switching arrangements. The remaining coloured conductors are often used as control wires serving factory machinery or other specialised applications.

Exercise 2.4

Conductors and insulating materials

1. For this practical exercise you will need the co-operation of your college's electrical store. In the table on page 100, list six electrically conductive components or accessories used in electrical installation engineering which may be found in your materials store. As an example, the first one has been done for you.

Conductive material	Used for/as . . .
1. Steel	Used to form an adaptable box for steel conduit/work
2.	
3.	
4.	
5.	
6.	

2. This is an exercise based on observation and understanding.
   (a) Look around your home, college or local library to find six different insulators of electricity which are not listed in the table on p. 98.
   (b) Write down your findings in the space provided for you. As an example, the first one has been done for you.

	Type of insulating material	Used for/as . . .
1	Bakelite®	A cover for an old type of rewirable fuseboard
2		
3		
4		
5		
6		

Materials used for cable sheathing

The role of the sheathing around a cable is to protect the conductors from mechanical damage or, in the case of screened metallic sheathing, to guard against any electromagnetic effects or stray inductive circuits. Screening is most important if sensitive circuitry is to be protected.

The table shows a selection of materials commonly used for cable sheathing.

Material	Application
PVC	General installation work and domestic cabling. Applied also to steel wire armoured cables. CABLE SHEATH — pvc
Steel or aluminium tape	Steel taped sheathing can be found on certain types of underground cables requiring wiped-lead jointing techniques. Modern aluminium taped sheathing is often polythene insulated and applied to instrumentation and communication circuits in industrial plants. Reproduced by kind permission of Walsal Conduits Ltd.
Seamless copper	Applied to mineral insulated cables. The sheath acts as a means for mechanical protection and will screen out stray inductive currents. The copper sheath is also used as a current protective conductor.
Aluminium with PVC sheath	Used in environmental control systems serving industrial complexes and office blocks. Used in the production of energy management service cables (EMS) and can also be used in data and signal transmission cables. Aluminium has also been used as the sheath of mineral insulated cables (MI). Reproduced by kind permission of Walsal Conduits Ltd.
Braided screened/PVC	Used for computer and date transmission. The screen is designed to filter out stray inductive currents. Reproduced by kind permission of Walsal Conduits Ltd.
Polychoroprene neoprene rubber	Used for the sheathing of cable supplying mobile and portable equipment in industrial complexes. PCP neoprene is both flame retardant and oil resistant.

Material	Application
Steel wire armouring (SWA)	Used as mechanical protection and may also be employed as a current protective conductor. Cables designed with stranded wire armour can be placed underground or used for general industrial applications.  Reproduced by kind permission of Walsal Conduits Ltd.

Exercise 2.5

Cable sheathing

For this practical exercise you will be shown three sample lengths of any of the following numbered cables:

• Mineral insulated (MI)
• PVC insulated and sheathed
• Steel wire armoured
• Neoprene rubber
• Screen computer and data transmission cable

(a) Discuss with your assessor the role the sheathing plays in respect to each of the sample cables provided.
(b) Suggest ways in which each type of cable may be used.
(c) Write down your conclusions in the table below.

Cable reference number	Type of cable	Role of sheathing
1.		
2.		
3.		

Cable termination methods

Socket outlets

Due to inexperience, many types of mistakes can be made when connecting conductors to a socket outlet. For example, too much outer sheathing may be stripped back or the conductors might be placed in an awkward way inside the socket box.

Listed below are more possible mistakes that should be avoided when connecting and terminating cables using clamped connections.

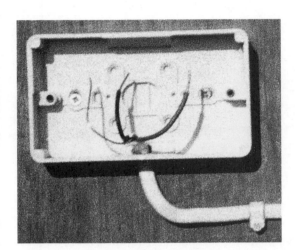

Conductors too short.

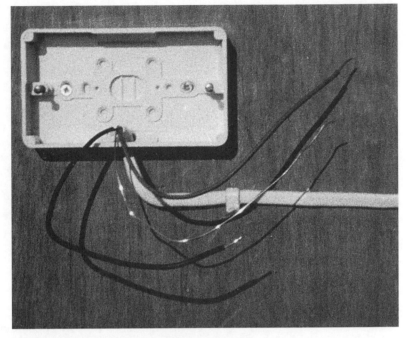

Conductors too long.

- Cables not fixed in a sensible way to serve the accessory.
- Not enough slack on all conductors causing strain on the terminals.
- Terminals not tightened enough, making them mechanically unsound.
- Far too much insulation removed from the conductor at the point of termination.
- Damaged or '**knife-sliced**' insulation inside the socket outlet box.
- No green/yellow oversleeving to serve the **current protective conductor** (cpc) or rubber cable entry grommet.

Stripping the outer sheath

Use a sharp knife or a pair of wire cutters, but be careful to avoid damage to the conductors, inner insulation and yourself.

Adhere to the following points when making a positive termination:

1. First cut the sheathed insulation between the conductors to a depth of about 40 mm as shown here.

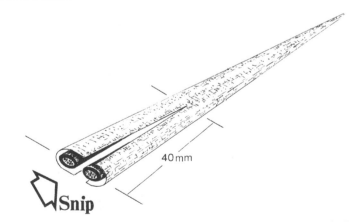

40 mm

Snip

Snip or cut the sheathing between the conductors to a distance of 40 mm.

2. Next pull apart both pieces of the cut cable sheath to the required length.
3. Run a sharp knife around the outer sheathing where it is to be removed as shown. Do not cut the inner insulation serving the conductor.
4. Remove the unwanted PVC sheath by sharply pulling from the uncut and existing cable sheath.

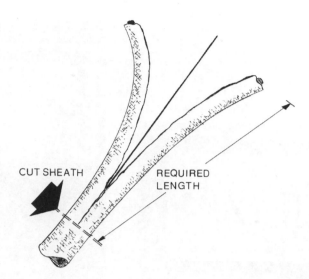

CUT SHEATH   REQUIRED
LENGTH

Lightly cut around the outer sheathing where it is to be removed.

Preparing for termination

1. Using adjustable wire strippers remove 10 mm of insulation from the end of each conductor. If required, trim carefully so that waste copper falls to the floor and does not become a hazard by flying in the wrong direction.
2. The inner insulation should always be removed carefully without cutting, denting or damaging the exposed copper conductor.
3. If only one conductor is to be placed into a terminal, it is wise to fold over the exposed copper. In this case, double the amount of inner insulation to be removed and fold over the exposed conductor as shown. Clamp the conductors using the terminal screw.

FOLD

CONDUCTOR

Double the amount of insulation to be removed and
fold over the bare copper conductor.

Terminating flexible cables

Woven braided cables, which are often used for chandeliers, table and standard lamps, often become frayed at the point of termination. This problem can be solved by one of the following:

1. Place expandable rubber sleeving near to the end of each conductor.
2. Heat shrink sleeving may be placed near to the end of each conductor. The sleeving is then shrunk by using a hot-air blower.
3. **Bitumastic/wax** compounds can be smoothed over the frayed braid.

The method chosen would depend upon the amount of time and money allowed for the job.

Clamping conductors at the point of termination

Conductors must be mechanically and electrically sound when placed inside the terminals. A loose connection will give trouble when current is drawn and arcing will occur (arcing is visible electrical discharge). Once this has started it is only a matter of time before the accessory is burnt or destroyed.

Over-tightening can cause the terminal screw to shear off making it impossible to remove the conductor from the terminal housing. If this happens the cable must be cut from the switch or socket and a new accessory fitted.

Another practical mistake is to leave far too much copper exposed at the point of termination.

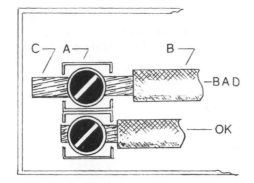
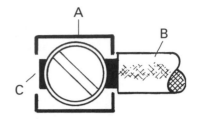

Never leave too much copper exposed at the point of termination. A = terminal point; B = insulation; C = too much bare copper conductor.

The correct way to terminate a conductor. A = terminal guard box; B = conductor; C = termination point.

Aluminium conductors

Aluminium is softer than copper and will break easily. Care must be taken when terminating aluminium conductors as the terminal screw could break through the wire. This may not be apparent until the installation has been switched on and faults occur.

The removal of too much outer sheath

When a socket is terminated it is important to leave enough slack cable inside the accompanying socket box. This is to make sure that no unnecessary strain is placed on the terminated conductors. Care must be taken to avoid too much cable slack and cramming it inside the box; otherwise trouble might occur in two ways:

1. A short circuit could occur inside the metal box if the conductors scuff the inner walls. (A short circuit is when direct contact is made between the live conductor and earth, or between the live and neutral conductors.)
2. The fixing screws serving the accessory can puncture the insulation of the conductor causing a **neutral** or **phase** to earth fault inside the socket box. Occasionally both red and black conductors are damaged, causing a direct short circuit through the metal box.

Measuring the correct length of cable needed

Place each conductor towards the furthest bottom point of the pressed steel accessory box, add 20 mm and cut the conductor as shown here.

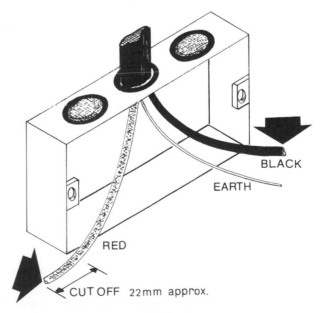

Measuring the correct length of cable to serve an accessory.

Once the accessory has been terminated, place all conductors well away from the steel fixing lugs and gently position the socket or switch for fixing to the steel box. Arranging the conductors sensibly will help to prevent any future problems.

Cable routing

Consider the following points:

1. Cables inside a loft space should always be clipped so that they are less likely to be disturbed.

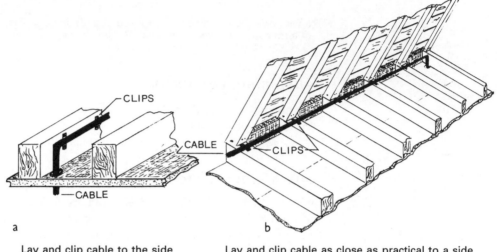

a

Lay and clip cable to the side
of the timber joists.

b

Lay and clip cable as close as practical to a side
which is near to a sloping roof.

2. In general **under-plaster cable routes** must be laid from above the top of a ceiling to the accessory in a straight vertical line. However, cable runs can be laid from underneath the floor and run in a similar fashion to serve the accessory. Usually the cables are then covered with suitable protection such as plastic or steel capping. Wiring in this way will allow wise decisions to be made about the positioning of nails to support picture frames or fitted wall units, etc., once the property has been handed over to the client.

Plastic or steel channelling provides protection whilst plastering
is carried out and enables rewiring at a later stage.

3. Surface cabling should be routed in vertical or horizontal runs. Keep all cables away from hot water pipes, data transmission cables, telephone wires and extra-low voltage circuits such as bells, alarm systems and computer wiring.
4. Never route at angles to the vertical or horizontal apart from the following exceptions:

   • Under-plaster cables routed to wall lights are usually placed at about 70° to the horizontal. This is because modern wall light fittings often have their fixing holes placed vertically, top and bottom. To avoid damage it is necessary to wire in the method described.

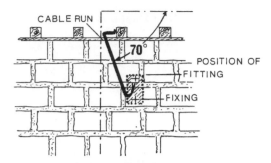

A cable serving a wall light is routed at an angle of 70°.
This will avoid damage to the cable when fixing the luminaire to the wall.

• Hob and oven cable-outlet accessories are wired as shown here. As the main switch serving the oven or hob is so near the service outlet cable, it is considered very uneconomical to wire in the usual way.

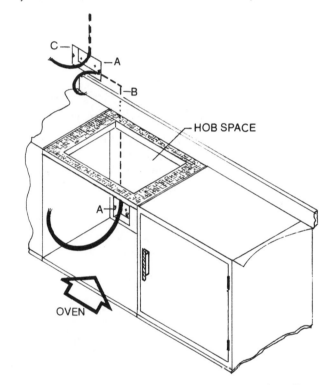

Hob and oven cable-outlet accessories. A = cable accessory box; B = path of cable, to be routed at right angles; C= control switch and supply cable for hob/oven.

Exercise 2.6   *Cables and terminations*

1. (a) What is the advantage of leaving enough slack when terminating cables. Write your answer in the space below.

  (b) Describe below the disadvantage of leaving too much slack, when for example a socket outlet is connected to incoming cables forming part of a **final ring circuit** (also known as a **ring main**).

2. List five precautions taken when preparing cables for termination. As an example the first one has been completed for you.

1. Precautions taken against damage to the insulation.

2.

3.

4.

5.

3. Indicate in the spaces below whether the following statements are true or false.

   (a) Cables serving roof spaces may be laid and routed in any fashion provided they are clipped.
   (b) Surface cabling must routed and clipped either vertically or horizontally.
   (c) As cables covered by plaster cannot be seen, general wiring may be routed diagonally.

   (a)   (b)   (c)

4. State, using your own words, two exceptions to the vertical/horizontal cable routing rule.

5. For this practical exercise you will need the following items:

   • A twin moulded (PVC) 13 amp socket outlet
   • A twin moulded surface socket box
   • Approximately 300 mm of 2.5 mm^2 PVC insulated and sheathed cable
   • Approximately 120 mm of green/yellow oversleeving to cover the bare current protective conductor
   • Two small wood-screws (say, $\frac{3}{4}$" × no. 8)
   • Two suitable cable clips for 2.5 mm^2 twin and earth cable
   • A wooden work-board

   (a) Arrange the listed items as shown here after selecting the items correctly.

   (b) Use wire or side cutters to correctly cut the outer sheath and conductors to a suitable length.
   (c) Remove an appropriate amount of inner insulation without damage to the exposed copper conductor. Make sure that the exposed copper is of a suitable length for the required termination.

(d) Check that all terminations are both electrically and mechanically sound.

(e) Provide the recommended amount of cable slack so that there is no strain on the terminations.

Demonstrate to your assessor that you can prepare and terminate a cable serving a twin 13 amp socket outlet. Remember the guide-lines on the previous pages.

6. For this exercise your tutor will give you a small length of **woven braided flexible cable**, which has been purposely frayed at one end.

Using expandable or heat-shrink sleeving, bitumastic/wax compounds or PVC adhesive tape, demonstrate to your assessor that you are able to carry out the following tasks:

(a) Make good the frayed ends of the flexible cable and remove 10 mm of the inner insulation. Allow 4 mm of inner insulation to be seen before remedial work is carried out.

(b) Show how the other end of the cable can be prevented from becoming frayed.

7. For this exercise you will need PVC-insulated and sheathed cable (1.0 mm^2, 1.5 mm^2, 2.5 mm^2 or 6.0 mm^2), cable clips to suit the cable required and PVC or steel channelling, sometimes referred to as 'capping'.

Assessment for this exercise will take place in a simulated work enviroment or in the workplace.

Demonstrate to your assessor that you are able to carry out the following tasks:

(a) Neatly route (smoothing the cable out as you progress) PVC-insulated and sheathed cable on finished plaster or timber to serve an electrical accessory.

- The cable must be correctly routed and connected to an electrical accessory
- No inner insulation must be visible outside the accessory box
- Terminals must be mechanically and electrically sound
- Sufficient slack must be left inside the box to avoid strain on the terminals

(b) Neatly route a PVC-insulated and sheathed cable to serve a sunken steel accessory box where cabling is to be covered by plaster.

- The cable must be correctly routed and placed in a steel accessory box, into which a rubber grommet has been inserted
- Use PVC or steel channelling to cover the cable and fix to the wall by means of masonry nails

Joint box terminations

Remember the following rules, which when followed can, with practice, produce a professional finish:

1. Never use cables that are too large. A 30 amp joint box will accommodate 1.0, 1.5, 2.5, 4.0 and 6.0 mm^2 conductors.

2. Always 'tailor-make' the length of your conductor to serve the chosen terminal. Be neat.

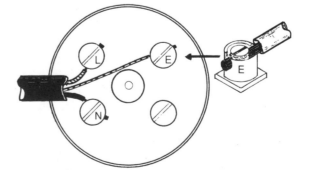

Cut the conductor to serve the terminal with the minimum of excess cable within the joint/junction box. L = live; N = neutral; E = earth.

3. Never cram unnecessary lengths of cable into a junction box. Not only is it unprofessional and unsightly but the excess cable will hinder cables that are to be inserted afterwards.

4. Place the outer sheath of the cable about 5 mm into the joint box. The inner insulation serving the copper conductor must never be visible outside the junction box. This rule also applies to socket outlets, ceiling roses, switches and fused connection units, etc.

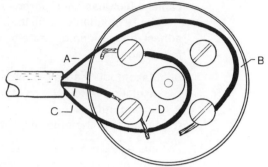

The wrong way to connect a junction box.
A = inner cable visible outside the juntion box; B = conductors ranged badly;
C = sheath removed outside of the junction box exposing the inner insulation;
D = too much copper conductor exposed either side of the terminal point.

5. Remove the outer sheath as described in previous paragraphs.

6. Remove sufficient inner insulation so that the bare copper conductor will fit safely inside the terminal housing of the junction box. Never remove too much inner insulation as this could cause problems in the future.

7. Make sure that all terminal screws are both electrically and mechanically sound. Loose terminals will cause arcing when on load. Arcing produces heat, which will lead to a gradual breakdown of the cable insulation and soften the copper conductor.

8. Fit the lid of the junction box securely and in the correct way.

9. All terminals must be both accessible and sound and able to withstand the design current (the current that will be flowing in the circuit). Twenty amp joint boxes are used for lighting circuits; 30 amp joint boxes are used for power installations.

10. Fix a circuit destination lable on the lid. This will help others who follow. Do not forget to fit oversleeving on the earth wire.

| Exercise 2.7 | *Electrical junction boxes* |

1. Why is it sensible to measure each conductor to the required length when cable connections are made inside a junction box?

2. State briefly below why the inner insulation serving a conductor should not be visible outside a junction box when the cable used is PVC-insulated and sheathed.

3. List two reasons why it is necessary to make sure that all connections are both electrically and mechanically sound and must be able to withstand the design current of the circuit.

4. In the space provided:

(a) State two different power ratings for domestic joint boxes.

(b) What physical differences would you expect to see?

5. For this practical exercise you will need the following:

- One 30 amp domestic joint box
- Two 150 mm lengths of 2.5, 4.0, or 6.0 mm² twin PVC-insulated and sheathed cable
- Approximately 120 mm of small bore green/yellow PVC oversleeving to cover the current protective conductor (the earth wire)
- Two suitable cable clips to suit the chosen cable
- Two $\frac{3}{4}$" × no. 8 wood-screws
- A wooden work-board (or insulated)
- Tools: suitable screwdrivers, side cutters, wire strippers

Screw the 30 amp junction box to the middle of your work-board.

Demonstrate to your assessor that you are able to terminate the two lengths of selected power cable as a through joint. This will mean that the red conductor will be connected to the red conductor, both black conductors will be connected together and both current protective conductors will be made common with each other.

(a) Use your side cutter correctly when removing the outer insulation. Do not damage the inner insulation.

(b) Measure, cut and terminate each conductor.

(c) Remove the exact amount of inner insulation without damaging the exposed copper conductor.

(d) Make sure that there is no excess cable inside the box.

(e) Ensure that there is no inner insulation visible outside the joint box.

(f) Check that all terminations/terminals are both electrically and mechanically sound.

(g) Let your assessor know the size of cable you have chosen.

Common types of cable termination

There are many different sorts of cable terminations, which are used for various jobs. A selection of the more common types of cable terminations found in electrical engineering today are shown in the table below.

Type	Information	Application
Bus-bar terminations	Tinned copper or bare copper	Securing heavy cables to copper distribution bus bars. Bus-bar terminations. A = copper bus bars; B = cable lug rest; C = steel bolt; D = steel nut. (Sometimes brass is used in place of steel.)

Type	Information	Application
Cable lugs	Tinned copper	Cable terminations serving large switches, earthing conductors, bus-bar distribution. Cable lug-compression type. (Reproduced by kind permission of Walsal Conduits Ltd.)
Pin terminations	Colour coded by size. Cable and termination is crimped together	A male crimped termination is pushed into a female 'bullet termination'. Often found in motor vehicle circuitry. **Male Bullet** **Female Bullet** **Pin** Pin terminations. (Reproduced by kind permission of Walsal Conduits Ltd.)
Screwed terminations	Block connector strips made from polyethylene, nylon or rigid Bakelite.® Various current ratings	General use in electrical engineering. Special types are made for use with printed circuit boards (PCB). flexible polyethylene Bakelite (rigid) nylon Screw terminations, sometimes known as strip connectors, for general use in electrical installation engineering. (Reproduced by kind permission of Walsal Conduits Ltd.)

Type	Information	Application
Crimped tag terminations	Colour coded in three sizes: Red, 0.75–1.5 mm² conductor. Blue, 1.5–2.5 mm² conductors. Yellow, 4.0–6.0 mm² conductors.	For terminating flexible or stranded conductors for various applications. Examples: earth points, terminals serving electric motors, etc. Connected by crimping the body of the termination to the bare conductor. Many types: fork, push-on spade, and ring type, etc. **Fork** **Push-on** **Push-on Adaptor "Piggy Back"** **Push-on Tab** **Ring** Pre-insulated tag terminations. (Reproduced by kind permission of Walsal Conduits Ltd.)
Cable terminations, soldered type	Made from copper that has been factory tinned. Termination made with use of solder.	For terminating conductors serving heavy switch gear, etc. A B Cable terminations, soldered type. A = Reservoir for liquid solder; B = service hole.

Type	Information	Application
Tunnel terminations	Crimped type insulated: colour coded in three sizes. Used like tag terminations. Crimped un-insulated type: made from soft copper that has been split lengthways to allow ease of crimping.	Often used as part of a jointing kit for steel wire armoured cables that are to be laid directly in the ground. Jointing by crimped tunnel terminations suspended within an epoxy resin filler in a purpose-made container. 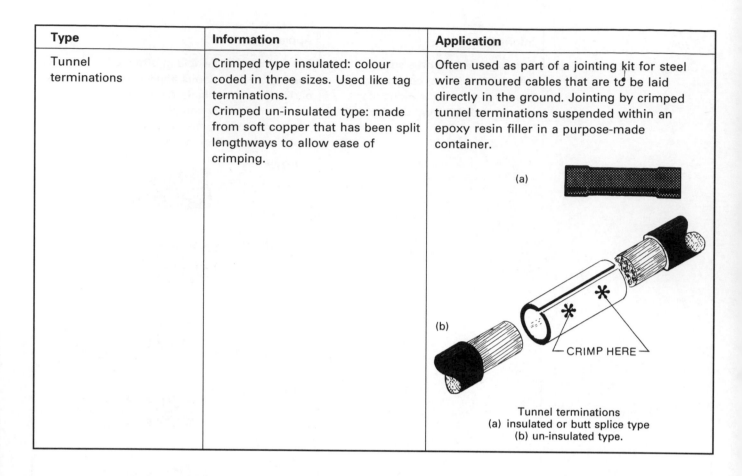 Tunnel terminations (a) insulated or butt splice type (b) un-insulated type.

Cable termination guide-lines

1. The size of a cable termination reflects its current carrying ability. A large terminal will carry a large amount of current whereas a small terminal will carry a small amount of current.
2. It is important to know the **rating** of the terminal so that any problems caused by excess current (for example, heat) can be avoided.
3. Terminals rated too low for the current they carry will become damaged and eventually burn out, destroying the insulation around the copper conductor.

Accessibility

The accessibility of terminations and junction boxes is very important. For example, it would be foolish to place a joint box supplying kitchen sockets under a tiled floor or in an area that would become inaccessible when building work is finished.

It must be easy to access junction boxes and earth termination points so that they are available for testing purposes, fault finding and general extensions to the installation.

When a joint box is opened for inspection check that all terminations are undamaged, electrically and mechanically sound, and that the box is not broken or cracked.

The quality of the termination

Below is a list pointing out how careless work can affect the quality of the termination.

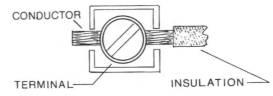

It is bad practice to expose too much bare conductor either side of a termination.

1. Far too much exposed bare conductor showing beyond the point of termination.
2. By undertightening the termination causing damage through arcing when on load.
3. By using the wrong size screwdriver and causing damage to the terminal screw.
4. By using blunt or damaged tools.
5. By overtightening and causing the machine screw to rotate on itself inside the terminal housing.
6. By heat caused by loose terminals and arcing. This softens the terminal point and reduces its mechanical strength.

Avoid using blunt or damaged tools; they can cause many practical problems.

Exercise 2.8

Junction boxes and terminations

1. Describe in the space below when you would use the following terminations

(a) Pin terminals
(b) Insulated tunnel terminals
(c) Strip connector terminations (screwed terminations)

2. List two problems that might happen due to loose terminals serving heavy current rated appliances.

3. Would the most suitable place for a 30 amp junction box be:

(a) buried under a concrete floor?
(b) in a roof space near to the loft entrance?
(c) safely buried inside the plaster-line of a wall?

4. Describe below how damage can occur to a terminal screw while preparing a junction box.

5. For this practical exercise you will require the following:

• One four-terminal 20 amp junction box
• 450 mm of 1.0 mm^2 lighting grade PVC-insulated and sheathed cable

- Two ¾" (19 mm) no. 8 wood-screws
- Six 1 mm size cable clips
- Approximately 150 mm of green/yellow oversleeving
- Approximately 25 mm of red oversleeving to suit the size of the conductor
- A wooden or insulated work-board

The final arrangement of components will be as shown here. Demonstrate to your assessor that you are able to wire a lighting junction box as follows:

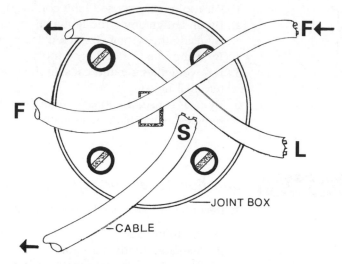

F = feed/supply; L = cable to the light; S = cable to the switch.

(a) Connect the **black** conductor of cable F (the **'feed'** or **'supply'** cable) to the **black** conductor of cable L (the cable to the light).

(b) Now connect the **red** conductor of cable F to the **red** conductor of cable S – the cable that would serve a switch.

(c) Using **red** oversleeving, sleeve the **black** conductor of cable S and connect to the **red** conductor of cable L.

(d) Sleeve all current protective conductors with green/yellow oversleeving and connect together in a suitable terminal.

(e) Use the cable clips to neatly secure the three cables to the work-board.

(f) Check that the conductors are correctly terminated and securely clamped.

(g) Make sure that no inner insulation is visible outside the junction box and that all conductors are neatly placed inside the box.

(h) Use the correct tools when preparing the junction box.

(i) Check that you have removed enough inner insulation to suit the terminal without damaging the bare copper conductor.

Soldering techniques

Soldering is a process of melting a soft metal, usually **lead–tin alloy,** over and between two wires, or between one wire and a printed circuit board in order to form an electro-mechanical joint.

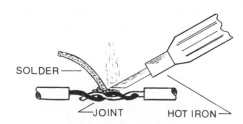

Soldering is a process of melting a soft lead–tin alloy over and between two wires which are to be bonded together.

Twisting bare wires together to form mechanical joints can be a satisfactory method of bonding two conductors together for a short period of time. When a joint needs to be permanent, solder will have to be applied. This is because copper wires will react with **oxygen** in the atmosphere, leading to a chemical process known as **oxidation**. The oxide formed over the wires creates an electrical resistance between the joint and reduces current flow in the circuit. Soldering will prevent this problem by protecting the joint from oxidation.

Solder is never used on a joint by applying it on the tip of a soldering iron, apart from an **autofeed iron** (see later). The wires are heated to a working temperature and the solder is then applied to the pre-heated joint. This will be fully described on p. 126.

Types of soldering irons and their uses

There are several different types of soldering irons and choice will depend on the cost and the intended use. A selection of irons commonly used in electrical engineering is given in the table below. The gauge of the solder to be used will be in proportion to the size of the bit.

Type of soldering iron	Use and relevant comments
Autofeed	Often used for production work involving a continuous process. Solder wire is automatically fed to a heated soldering tip where it is applied to the workpiece. (110 or 230 volts)
Cordless	Gas operated (butane gas) or heated by a rechargeable heavy-duty battery. Used by field engineers where there is no access to mains electricity.
Hobbest	Low wattage 'throw away' type. Ideal for the occasional task, or hobbest electronics work. (230 volts)
Miniature	Often used in the workshop to solder **surface mounted devices** by hand. (Low wattage, 230 volts)
Soldering station	Used by professionals. Temperature controlled is 20°C steps between approximately 150 and 470°C. Replacement parts available. Suitable for most applications by changing the soldering tip, sometimes referred to as a **bit**. Can be expensive. (110 and 230 volts)
Soldering gun	Used for fast heat applications. Reaches the maximum tip temperature in under 10 seconds. The gun is designed to provide intermittent power. (Used on 230 volt mains supply.)
Variable temperature	Ideal where temperature control is required but where a soldering station would be impractical. A small bladed screwdriver is used to set the working temperature. (230 volts)

Voltages

There are many different types of soldering irons, each of which must be used for a particular voltage. The four most common voltages used for soldering irons in industry are:

1. 230 volts AC for workshop use
2. 110 volts AC for site work
3. 50 volts AC for production areas, motor vechicle repair workshops
4. 12–24 volts DC field tasks

Power ratings

Power ratings vary but are usually proportional to the size of the appliance. Miniature mains soldering irons are usually **rated** at 15 watts (they provide 15 watts of power), whereas hobbyist irons are 25 watts and professional soldering stations are between 35 and 40 watts. The professional type can be thermostatically set for the intended task. Large heavy-duty irons can be rated as high as 100 watts but these are not often found in electronic workshops.

| Exercise 2.9 | *Basic techniques – soldering* |

1. State in the space provided whether the following statements are true or false.

   (a) Molten solder must be dispensed from the soldering iron to the joint to be soldered.
   (b) A soldering station is an ideal tool for most soldering tasks.

   (a) True/False

   (b) True/False

2. This is a pre-soldering exercise. You will be shown several different types of numbered soldering irons of which ONE will be more suitable than the others for soldering **20 standard wire gauge** conductors together (20 SWG wire is approximately 0.65 mm in cross-sectional area).

   Select the iron most suitable and record this in the table provided, adding your comments as to why the iron was chosen.

Soldering iron reference number	Comments
1.	
2.	
3.	
4.	

Soldering bits: sizes and shapes

The following table illustrates eight types of **interchangeable** soldering bits and their uses.

Profile of soldering bit	Uses
45° ◯ I 4.75	Soldering large joints, turret lugs, cable tags, etc.
45° ● I 3.2	General purpose where additional heat is required.
45° ● I 1.5	Printed circuit board work. Soldering small electronic components.
45° ● I 2.3	Used for soldering large electronic components such as power transistors, etc.
⊙	Heavy-duty uses such as transformers and large industrial capacitors.
⊗ I 3.2 0.4	Heavy-duty general purpose soldering such as joints, lugs, large components, etc.
⊗ I 2.4 0.7	Applied to heavier electronic components such as transformers and power diodes, etc.
⊗ I 1.0 0.4	Work of a delicate nature such as small components and printed circuit boards.

Types of solder and their uses

Solder is an alloy (a mixture of two or more metals) consisting of approximately 80% **tin** and 20% **lead** and is used to join metals together. **Soft solder**, used for electrical and electronic work, will melt between 200° and 300°C. Hard solder contains quantities of **silver** mixed with the alloy and is often refered to as **silver solder**. Brazing solder, an alloy of **zinc** and **copper**, melts at a temperature of over 800°C and is used to join copper surfaces together permanently. Many solder wires used in

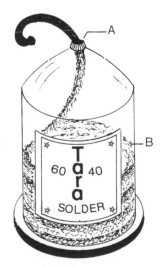

Rosin-core solder from a dispenser. A = dispense port; B = solder coil.

electrical work are **rosin cored** and additional **flux** is not required. Flux will be dealt with later on p. 121. Rosin-cored solder consists of 60% tin and 40% lead and is ideal for general electrical tasks that need careful handling.

The characteristics of solder can be changed at the manufacturing stage by the introduction of small amounts of **sulphur**, **arsenic** or **bismuth**. This solder is used for special purposes and not for general use.

Solder can be obtained for electrical purposes either as a reel, a stick, or with a dispenser.

Reel solder (left). Solder wire dispenser (right)
(Reproduced by kind permission of RS Components Ltd.)

There are many different types of solder but only a small selection is suitable for electrical work. In summary, the types of solder are as follows.

1. General purpose solder for electrical use

Electrical solder, 40% lead, 60% tin, is used for electrical connections. This type of solder has **no tensile strength** and must be used with a flux (either built into the solder or applied separately) to prevent oxidation.

Some types of electrical solder are known as **water soluble solders**. This means that any flux left over from soldering a joint can be washed off with water instead of using harmful **chlorofluorocarbon** (CFC) based cleaners.

Flexible wire solder can be obtained in three different popular standard wire gauges to suit the task in hand (18, 22 and 24 SWG). Other gauges that are available are 14 and 16 SWG.

- For soldering small components and wires use 18 SWG wire solder.
- Use 22 or 24 SWG wire solder for medium-sized jobs, such as connecting large power transistors.
- The largest diameter wire solder, 16 SWG, is ideal for electrical engineering applications.

Other general purpose tin-lead alloy solders are supplied with several cores of **non-corrosive flux**. This removes the need to apply flux to the molten solder.

2. Lead-free solder

This type of solder comprises 99% **tin** and 1% **copper** and has several cores of built-in **halide** active **rosin flux**. It is made as an alternative to lead, which is toxic and is sometimes used by plumbers.

3. Aluminium solder

Aluminium solder is not normally used for electrical work. The solder is made from 80% **lead**, 18% **tin** and 2% **silver**. Flux may be applied separately or this type of solder can be obtained with a water soluble flux built into it. The melting point is approximately 178°C and it becomes fully molten at 270°C.

4. Plumbing solder

This type of solder is used for mechanically connecting copper pipes and fittings. Obtainable as a reel in 10 SWG, the solder is virtually lead-free, comprising 99.5% **tin** and 0.5% **copper**. The flux is applied separately as a smooth paste and is soluble in water. The melting point of plumbing solder is approximately 228°C.

Plumbing solder and smooth paste flux.
(Reproduced by kind permission of RS Components Ltd.)

5. Stick solder

This is a high purity solder, ideally suited for **solder baths** or **pots** (a device in which molten solder is kept for **tinning** component leads, tags and conductors, etc.). As with traditional electrical reel solder, stick solder is made from 40% **lead** and 60% **tin**.

When conductors are tinned, the bare copper wire is covered with a thin layer of solder to prevent oxidation. Tinned conductors are far easier to solder together than plain copper conductors.

Solder pot for tinning leads, tags, components and wires, etc. (Reproduced by kind permission of RS Components Ltd.)

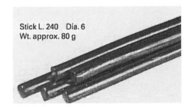

Stick solder: ideal for solder baths or pots. (Reproduced by kind permission of RS Components Ltd.)

6. Special use solders

- High melting-point solder; suitable for use where high or low temperatures are present.
- Low residue solder; comprising 60% **tin**, about 39.5% **lead** and 0.5% **halide flux**. This type of solder has a low **fuming odour**.
- Low melting-point solder; this type of solder comprises 62% **tin**, 36% **lead** and 2% **silver**, and has a melting point of 179°C.

Flux

When heat is applied to an electrical copper joint it will oxidise (oxygen will react with the copper to form a resistant film on the conductor). Therefore, it is necessary to use an **oxide remover**.

Soldering flux is an efficient way to remove the unwanted oxide and will allow the solder to bond with the copper wires. Never use flux containing **corrosive substances** for electrical work; it will cause problems at a later stage.

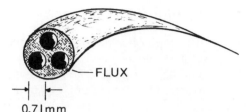

Three-core non-corrosive flux incorporated into 22 standard wire gauge (SWG) solder.

Flux is also used as a '**wetting agent**' as it promotes the liquidity of the solder.
Always use the most suitable standard wire gauged rosin-core solder for the
particular task. A useful guide is that it should be thick enough to solder a joint
in a couple of seconds without using an excessive length of solder-wire.

Types of electrical solder flux

1. **Rosin-based soldering flux**
   This flux is applied separately. It is a red jelly-like substance and is used for general
   purpose soldering and electrical work involving soldering. (Rosin is a yellowish resin
   obtained as a residue from the distillation of turpentine and dead pine wood.)
2. **Liquid rosin flux**
   This flux is non-flammable and is ideal for solder pot applications.
3. **Aerosol flux**
   This type of flux is used to spray onto soldered joints when heating to remove
   electronic components.

Types of non-electrical flux

1. **Plumbing flux**
   Plumbing flux takes the form of a smooth paste for use with copper and brass
   fittings for heating, water and gas services. Surfaces to be soldered do not require
   pre-cleaning. The flux paste is water soluble.

Diameters: solder

Solder wire is manufactured to **British Standard Wire Gauges** (SWG) and the
smaller gauges are ideally suited for lightweight electrical connections. It should be as
thin as possible but the diameter must always reflect the size of the task undertaken.
Ideally, 22 SWG solder wire is suitable for work involving printed circuit boards and
strip boards.
   Other sizes commonly used are:

- 10 SWG (diameter: 3.251 mm, 8.3019 in cross-sectional area)
- 16 SWG (diameter: 1.626 mm, 2.0755 in cross-sectional area)
- 18 SWG (diameter: 1.219 mm, 1.1675 in cross-sectional area)
- 24 SWG (diameter: 0.5588 mm, 0.2453 in cross-sectional area)
- 26 SWG (diameter: 0.4572 mm, 0.1641 in cross-sectional area)

The largest size listed (10 SWG) is a plumber's solder and is used for bonding copper
water pipes together.

Heat shunts

A **heat shunt** is a hand-held tool, which allows delicate components to be soldered
in circuit without fear of heat damage to the component. It may take the form of a
pair of **snipe-nose pliers**, a screwdriver blade, or a purpose-made **clip-on heat shunt**.
Placing the heat shunt between the component and the tip of the soldering iron will
allow excess heat to be absorbed, keeping the delicate component free from damage.

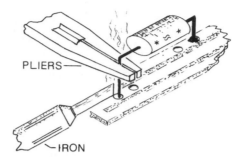

Snip-nose pliers can be used as a heat shunt.

Extraction and insertion tools

Extraction tools are purpose-made for a variety of uses, some of which you will not need to study. Uses include the following:

- Component extraction serving a printed circuit board
- Extracting studs from circuit boards
- Spring hooks for directing or claiming back awkwardly placed wires
- Tools to enable the correct positioning and extraction of contacts
- Tools to enable the extraction of direct-in-line (DIL) packages from DIL sockets.
  Tools called **inserters** are designed to insert DIL packages

Extractor and inserter tools for DIL packages.
(Reproduced by kind permission of RS Components Ltd.)

- Extraction tools for the safe removal of **plastic leaded chip carriers** (PLCC) from their sockets.
  (You will be shown how to use this type of tool during your course work.)

Exercise 2.10   *Solder and soldering accessories*

1. Decribe briefly what a 4.75 mm diameter soldering iron tip may be used for.

2. Using your own words, describe briefly in the space below how the characteristics of solder may be changed at the manufacturing stage.

3. A very delicate, thermally sensitive electronic component is to be soldered to a small printed circuit board. Which **two** of the following should be used to protect the component? Write your answer in the space below.

   (a) a suitable size fuse
   (b) a small 1.0 × 0.4 mm soldering bit or tip
   (c) a 4.75 mm size soldering bit or tip
   (d) a suitable heat shunt
   (e) use of 10 SWG soldering wire
   (f) adequate flux around the joint on the circuit board
   (g) a dry twisted joint (no solder)

4. Using your own words, state in the space provided two reasons why flux should be used when soldering electrical joints together.

5. How can oxidation be prevented when two copper conductors are joined together using solder?

6. For this practical exercise you will be shown the following numbered items:

   • Three different sizes of soldering irons or interchangeable bits
   • Four common sizes of solder wire
   • 50 mm of 20 SWG insulated copper wire
   • 50 mm of 1.0 mm² insulated copper cable
   • 50 mm of 2.5 mm² insulated copper cable

   This is a matching exercise.

   (a) Demonstrate to your assessor that you are able to match correctly both solder wire and iron/bit to the cable/wire provided. For the purpose of this exercise, imagine that two identical conductors are to be solder jointed together.
   (b) Record the items matched in the table provided.

Size of gauge of wire or cable size	Reference number of soldering iron or interchangeable bit	Gauge of solder to use (SWG)
20 SWG		
1.0 mm²		
2.5 mm²		

7. This exercise is to test your knowledge of various types of soldering fluxes. You will be shown three types; each will be reference numbered.

   (a) Demonstrate that you are able to recognise each of the fluxes offered to you.
   (b) Describe their uses to your assessor.
   (c) Write your answers in the table provided.

Flux no.	Type of flux	Corrosive/ Non-corrosive	Application
1.			
2.			
3.			

8. For this practical exercise you will require the use of a general purpose inserter and extractor tool. Each tool should be able to cater for direct-in-line packages up to 16 way. A direct-in-line (DIL) package together with a compatible socket will also be required.

An inserter is designed to pick up a DIL package and align it to the correct insertion distance. Once positioned, the inserter can be activated to place the DIL package correctly into the DIL socket provided. You will have been shown how to do this in your course work.

(a) Demonstrate to your assessor that you are able to perform this task in the correct way.

(b) Demonstrate that you are able to remove the DIL package from its socket with the extractor tool provided.

Safety precautions for using solder

Listed in random order below are safety precautions that should be observed when soldering is carried out:

1. Before work is started check the condition of the flexible lead serving the soldering iron.
2. Care should be taken not to burn yourself or the workpiece.
3. Always place the iron in the spiral cradle provided when resting. This will reduce the risk of fire caused by carelessness.
4. Avoid breathing in fumes generated by the hot flux and molten solder. Lead is poisonous!
5. Keep volatile cleaning fluids away from heated surfaces and soldering iron tips.
6. Always switch off the soldering iron and withdraw from the power socket when not in use.
7. Check for broken or cracked soldering iron handles.
8. Occasionally check to make sure that the terminals serving the plug are secure and that the correct size fuse has been fitted.
9. Keep the hot tip of the iron well away from the flexible supply cable.

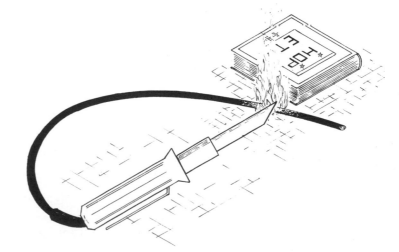

Always place the soldering iron away from combustible materials when not in immediate use.

10. Take care when handling heat shunts after use; they can become very hot.
11. Never flick excess hot molten solder from the tip of the soldering iron. Always use a damp sponge.
12. When **desoldering** is undertaken, use safety glasses to protect the eyes.
13. Replace worn soldering iron tips/bits when necessary.
14. Never file copper-plated steel soldering bits. Replace if damage is caused.

Soft soldering

Soft soldering techniques are used for electrical and electronic project work when permanent joints are required. As the name suggests, the solder used is soft when compared with other types of solder used for non-electrical applications.

The table below shows the advantages and the disadvantages of using soft solder.

Advantages	Disadvantages
1. A simple way of making a good electrical fluid joint.	1. Limited to electrical connections and metal-to-metal lap joints.
2. A limited number of tools are required.	2. Low in tensile strength.
3. Distortion is greatly reduced.	3. Not suitable for working temperatures greater than 100°C.
4. Metals that are dissimilar may be joined.	4. Soldering agent must be compatible with the metal to be soldered, otherwise bonding will not take place.
5. Soft solder will melt at low temperatures.	5. Poor conductive joints can be made if soldering is not carried out properly.

Soldering conductors

Planning, preparation and jointing

A concise step-by-step approach outlining the basic rules for soldering follows:

1. Clean the conductors that are to be soldered together.
2. Position the workpiece carefully.
3. Rest the workpiece on thermal insulation, if possible, so that heat loss is minimised.
4. Choose the correct type and gauge of solder for the task.
5. Choose the correct flux if rosin-core solder wire is not used.
6. Select the most suitable tinned soldering tip for the job, adjust the temperature control (200–300°C) and switch 'ON'. Make sure the soldering iron bit is clean and free from contamination. Use a tip cleaning pot for tinning and cleaning the iron-clad bits.

tip tinner/cleaner

Tip cleaner/tinner pot for bench-top use.
(Reproduced by kind permission of RS Components Ltd.)

7. Tin the clean conductors by offering the molten solder to the base of the conductor when the working temperature has been reached. After tinning has been carried out both conductors will appear clean and shiny from the deposited solder.

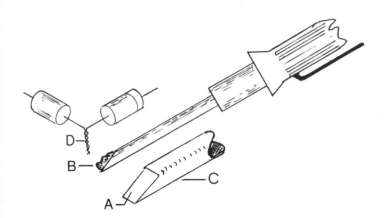

A splash of solder is applied to the working area (A) of the soldering iron. B = blob of solder; C = soldering bit; D = twisted and tinned conductors to be soldered.

BRIGHT & SHINY

SOLDER LINE

The right and wrong way of making a soldered joint: (a) satisfactory, (b) too much solder.

8. Gently twist together the tinned conductors that are to be solder-jointed.
9. Apply a splash of solder to the tip of the soldering iron and then offer the twisted joint to the tinned soldering iron bit.
10. Distribute the heat evenly over the twisted cables but do not overheat. If flux is used it must be applied sparingly.
11. The tinning on both conductors will melt into each other and make a reliable electrical connection.
12. Remove the soldering iron and wipe the excess solder from the tip onto a damp sponge. A cellulose sponge is usually included with the soldering station.
13. The finished joint should appear bright and shiny.
14. If additional solder has to be used to make the joint, use sparingly.
15. A suitable insulated '**heat-shrink**' sleeve can now be placed over the jointed conductors. Once securely in place, warm the heat-shrink insulation with a hot-air blower. The sleeving will rapidly shrink in size and provide a reliable means for insulating the jointed conductors.

Additional points

- If a joint appears dull and pitted, you must resolder.
- Keep cleanliness in mind when soldering.
- Never over-apply flux.
- Place the heated iron under the workpiece.
- Keep the solder in a constant fluid state.
- Use an **inserter tool** to position the component.
- Thermally insulating the item to be soldered will prevent heat loss.
- Use a heat shunt when considered necessary.
- Apply flux evenly over the surfaces to be soldered together.
- Never overheat the joint to be soldered.
- When required, use anti-static handling techniques to prevent damage to sensitive components.
- When using printed circuit boards, etc., always bend component leads neatly. Slightly bend the leads of the component after fitting into the PCB track holes to stop the component falling out when soldering.
- Leave a small gap between the soldered joint and the insulation to stop the insulation melting.

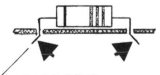

LEADS BENT

Bend the leads of the component after fitting into the circuit board. This will prevent the component from falling out when the board is turned over for soldering.

| Exercise 2.11 | *Soldering conductors and soft soldering* |

1. Why is it wise to keep volatile cleaning liquids away from hot soldering irons? Answer in the space below.

2. Fill in the partially completed table.

Problem	Remedy
Solder spikes	
Dull and pitted soldered joints	
Solder melts, but slowly	
Bad electrical continuity	

3. Why is it wise to leave a small gap between a soldered joint and the insulation serving the wire? Answer in the space below.

4. Suggest a way to prevent a component falling out of the holes serving a strip board before soldering takes place.

5. For this practical exercise you will required to **choose** the following components and materials:

- A suitable soldering iron for 20 SWG wire
- Suitable rosin-core solder wire for soldering 20 SWG wire
- 200 mm of insulated 20 SWG wire
- Wire stripper and cutter
- A small heat shunt
- Two 1 watt resistors of any value

Check that the equipment you have chosen is correct then demonstrate to your assessor that you are able to carry out the following practical exercise:

(a) Observe safety precautions.
(b) Remove 3 mm of insulation from each end of the wire.
(c) Check that each end of the bare copper is clean and free from contamination.
(d) Tin each end of the 20 gauge wire and the ends of each resistor.
(e) Solder the two resistors together in series formation (i.e. one after the other) and solder them to the two free ends of the 20 gauge wire to form a loop.
(f) Demonstrate the use of a heat shunt to protect the electronic components from excess heat.

Check that all terminations are mechanically and electrically sound and that there is no excessive solder, flux or any solder spikes. Check that a small gap is present between the wire insulation and the soldered joint.

Connecting and soldering wires to terminal posts

A four-step guide showing how a wire can be soldered to a terminal post providing electro-mechanical soundness to the installation is shown here. All components to be soldered must be cleaned and free from any contamination.

The tools and components are:

- wire stripper and cutters
- snipe-nose pliers
- cleaning fluid
- a section of strip board
- eye hole terminal posts (pre-tinned)
- rosin-core solder wire
- insulated wire

Place the terminal post into the strip board. Remove sufficient insulation from the wire and clean the heated iron bit using a damp sponge. Tin the soldering iron bit, heat the conductor and apply solder to tin the bare copper conductor. (Note that terminal posts are available in many different designs.)

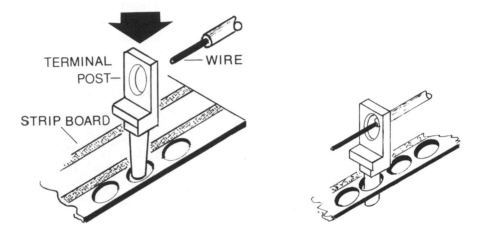

Insert the tinned conductor into the terminal hole.

Wrap the conductor around the terminal housing using a pair of snipe-nose pliers. Then, crush the tinned conductor against the terminal post to provide good surface-to-surface connection. Heat the terminal post to a working temperature and apply a dab of rosin-core solder to both the post and the tinned copper wire. A small space should be left between the soldered joint and the insulation serving the wire. Avoid overheating, excessive solder, flux and solder spikes. The finished joint or termination should look bright and shiny and should be free from '**pitting**'. If the soldered termination looks dull and has minute holes over its surface, the joint should be melted and re-worked.

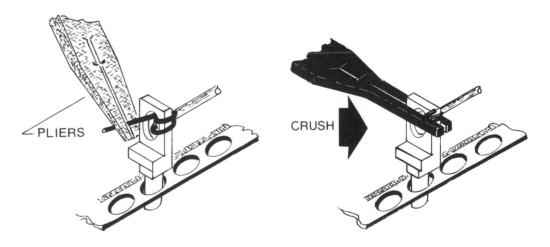

Remember to report any defects that show up in materials and tools to an appropriate person.

Exercise 2.12   *Terminating a conductor and soldering techniques*

1. Why is it necessary to tin a bare copper wire before soldering takes place? Write your answer in the space below.

2. For this practical exercise you will require the following:

   - 200 mm of insulated **20 gauge** wire
   - Snipe-nose pliers
   - Wire strippers/cutters
   - A soldering iron or bit suitable for the task
   - A small section of strip board
   - Three **'eye-hole'** terminal posts for strip board use
   - Rosin-core solder suitable for 20 gauge wire
   - A milliohm bench meter

   (a) Demonstrate to your assessor that you are competent in preparing and soldering a single insulated 20 gauge conductor to three strip board terminal posts.

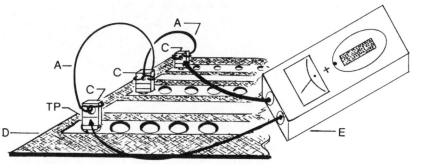

   A test must be made between the two outer terminal posts. A = insulated wire; TP = terminal posts; C = soldered joints; D = strip board; E = ohm or milliohm meter. The terminal posts must be soldered neatly to the strip board.

   (b) Once complete, measure the electrical resistance between the two outermost terminal posts using the milliohm meter provided. Select a low scale using the instrument's selector switch. Place the meter's test leads firmly against the two outermost terminal posts and read off the value obtained directly from the display scale. Record the value below. When soldered correctly the resistance of the conductor and soldered joints should be between 5 and 10 milliohms.

   The value in milliohms obtained from the three soldered terminations and the 20 SWG insulated wire is:

3. For this practical exercise, the following will be needed:

   - Multimeter
   - A section of strip board
   - Two press-fit terminal pins (T1 and T2)
   - 200 mm of flexible insulated wire (IW) (0.5 or 0.75 mm^2)
   - Four resistors (R1–R4)
   - Four diodes (D1–D4)
   - Wire cutters and strippers
   - Cleaning fluid
   - Two 'circuit board sized' capacitors (C1 and C2)
   - Solder and soldering station – please select

   (a) By referring to the following figure, demonstrate to your assessor that you are able to make good soldered joints without damaging the components. The figure is an exercise illustration and does not represent a working circuit.

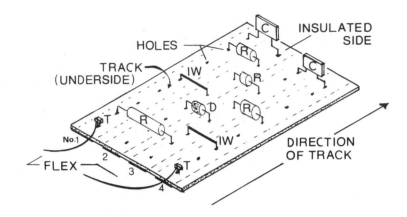

(b) Use a heat shunt where necessary.

(c) Select a suitable soldering iron, solder and bit size for the task.

(d) Remove the insulation correctly without damage to the conductor.

(e) Demonstrate to your assessor how conductor ends are tinned.

(f) Demonstrate to your assessor how components are fitted onto a strip board before soldering takes place.

(g) Demonstrate that all connections are mechanically and electrically sound.

4. For this exercise you will require the following:

- Rosin-core solder (select with supervision) and a multimeter
- A soldering station and a selection of interchangeable bits
- Two 150 mm lengths of 2.5 mm^2 insulated wire and a resistor

(a) Cut the insulated wire in half and demonstrate to your assessor that you can solder two insulated wires together without damage to the insulation.

(b) Once soldered, remove 5 mm of insulation from the two 'free' ends and solder the leads of a resistor between them as shown here.

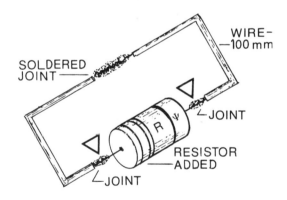

(c) Test for mechanical soundness and electrical continuity.

5. For this practical exercise you will require the following:

- Rosin-core solder (please select with supervision)
- A suitable soldering iron/station
- Two lengths of 2.5 mm^2 insulated wire

Demonstrate to your assessor that you are competent in carrying out the following tasks:

(a) Select a suitable soldering iron/bit for the task outlined in (c) below.

(b) Remove 10 mm of insulation from both ends of each length of wire without damaging the copper conductors.

(c) Tin all prepared ends of the 2.5 mm^2 conductors correctly, so that they are free from impurities, solder spikes, excessive solder and flux.

(d) The solder selected must be of a suitable type and gauge for the task.

(e) Produce a completed task, which has a bright appearance.

Circuit testing

This topic will be reviewed first as knowledge gained will be needed for future practical exercises.

Insulation testing

After an electrical installation has been completed, an **insulation resistance test** must be carried out before a permanent connection is made to the supply. This test will verify that the insulation serving the conductors and accessories, such as switches and socket outlets, are completely free from any possible fault condition between current-carrying conductors and any current-carrying conductor and earth.

Procedure

Before testing an installation, remove or disconnect all lamps and current-using equipment. The *Wiring Regulations* recommend that electronic devices should be completely isolated from circuit in order to avoid permanent damage to printed circuit boards and other higher voltage-sensitive electronic components.

With all switches 'ON' and fuses or circuit breakers placed in position, the total resistance recorded from the **insulation tester** must not fall below 0.5 megohms (500 000 ohms) when the declared (known as the 'nominal') voltage of the mains supply is no more than 500 volts. Above 500 volts, and up to 1000 volts, the minimum insulation resistance should not fall below 1 megohm (1 000 000 ohms). See Regulation 713–04–04.

Testing can be carried out in four easy stages. As an example, assume a three-phase and neutral installation is ready for examination.

Stage 1: Place the test leads into the instrument. Switch to the 500 volt insulation test range and measure the insulation resistance between all current-carrying conductors. This is achieved by pressing the instrument's '**test button**'. The value obtained should not be less than those values prescribed earlier.

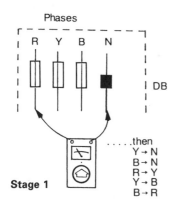

Insulation test between all current-carrying conductors. R = red phase (L1); Y = yellow phase (L2); B = blue phase (L3); N = neutral; DB = distribution board.

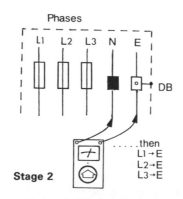

Test the insulation resistance between each current-carrying conductor and the principle protective conductor (E). All fuses/circuit breakers must be removed/switched off before testing commences.

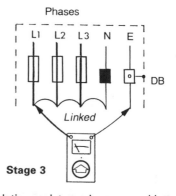

Insulation resistance is measured between grouped current-carrying conductors and the main protective conductor.

Stage 2: Next, test the insulation resistance between each current-carrying conductor and the main protective conductor (once known as the **earth wire**) as shown above. The value obtained in megohms should not fall below the values specified.

Stage 3: Finally check the **collective** resistance between the current protective conductor and all current-carrying conductors made common as outlined above. The value obtained should not be less than the value defined.

Stage 4: All tested connections must be identified and labelled to meet specified requirements.

A single-phase installation is tested in the same way as a three-phase installation but is less involved as there is only one phase and neutral conductor together with a current protective conductor to consider.

Voltage output

A typical insulation test meter, such as a **digital** model, has a test voltage output of 500 and 1000 volts. Other models are often equipped with three voltage ranges, 250, 500 and 1000 volts. The accuracy factor for this type of instrument is approximately ±1 digit or ±1.5% of the value obtained.

Obtaining unacceptable values

If the values obtained from the test instrument fall below the prescribed value, a check must be made to find the reason for the fault condition. The fault must always be remedied so that the level of insulation resistance is increased to an acceptable level.

Precautions

Insulation test instruments deliver high voltages and precautions must be taken when using them. These voltages are not lethal but they can cause a physical shock reaction.
   The following should be remembered:

- Keep hands dry.
- Do not touch the ends of the instrument's leads.
- Do not '**lock**' the test button in the 'ON' position when working at heights.
- Wear rubber electrically insulated gloves when testing is carried out in cramped conditions.
- After testing, touch both tested conductors together and to earth to discharge stored electricity (**capacitance**).

Exercise 2.13

Insulation testing

State in the space provided whether the following is true or false.
A typical insulation test instrument would have an output voltage of 500 volts with an accuracy factor of 1.5%.

Polarity testing

Before an electrical installation is permanently switched 'on' a **polarity test** must be carried out to check the following:

1. That each switch, fuse, circuit breaker and single pole (that is, switching only the 'live' conductor) controlling device is connected in the 'live' **phase** conductor.
2. That each socket outlet has been correctly wired, terminating the 'live' **phase** conductor in the terminal marked L.
3. That the central connection point of an '**Edison**' type lampholder is connected to the 'live' **phase** conductor, and that the outer threaded component is connected to the **neutral** conductor. See Regulation 713–09–01.

Procedure

This test must be carried out with all switches placed in the 'ON' position. Current-consuming equipment, such as heating appliances and lamps, etc., must be removed or disconnected. Fuses and/or circuit breakers must be withdrawn and the black **neutral** conductor serving the circuit under test must be disconnected from the neutral **terminal block** in the fuse board or distribution centre.

The outgoing red phase conductor under test originating from the top of the fuse or breaker should be temporarily linked directly to the **earth terminal block** serving the fuse board. The danger of '**reversed polarity**' is illustrated here.

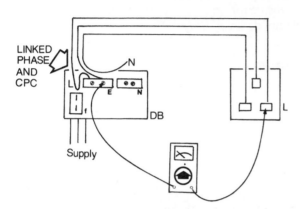

Before carrying out a polarity test, remove all fuses/circuit breakers and link the outgoing phase conductor(s) to the current protective conductor (cpc) and disconnect the neutral conductor(s) serving the circuit(s) under test. DB = distribution board.

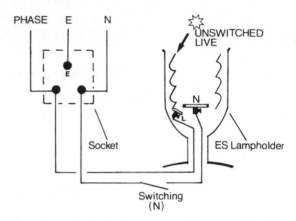

The phase conductor is permanently connected at the lampholder regardless of whether the switch is 'ON' or 'OFF'.

The polarity of electrical accessories can be tested using either a continuity meter (measuring ohms or parts of an ohm), or a combined bell and battery so wired that the bell will ring when the connecting wires are placed together. Place one connecting wire on the earth terminal in the distribution centre and the other to a switch terminal which is to be tested. If the polarity is correct a continuity meter will show a near **zero ohms** position or the bell will ring when using the combined bell and battery method. The further from the distribution centre, the greater the resistance appears on the continuity test meter. (Resistance is directly proportional to length.) After testing, reinstate all disconnected wires and replace fuses and breakers.

Exercise 2.14 | Polarity testing

1. State in the space below whether the following is true or false.
   Polarity testing is always carried out with all switches placed in the 'ON' position and current-consuming equipment left in circuit.

2. When polarity testing is carried out, what would happen if the red phase conductor had not been temporarily linked to the **earth** terminal block serving the distribution centre?

3. For this practical exercise you will require access to a simulated electrical installation.

   (a) Using a combined bell and battery set or a multimeter switched to the ohms scale, demonstrate that you are competent to carry out a polarity test on a simulated circuit.
   (b) Sockets may be unscrewed from the accessory box if this proves to be easier.
   (c) Fault conditions should be reported to an appropriate person.
   (d) Talk your way through each principal stage of the testing procedure.

Continuity testing

To check that all current protective conductors are electrically sound and securely connected, each conductor – whether forming part of a multicore cable or whether routed independently – must be tested.

Procedure

To test, securely attach a long stranded or flexible single cable to the **common** service terminal of a continuity meter. The accompanying lead will be the instrument's own test lead. There will now be a long and a short lead attached to the continuity tester.

Connect the bared end of the longest lead firmly into the earthing terminal block serving the distribution centre. This will allow freedom of movement to test all current protective conductors within the radius of the longest test lead.

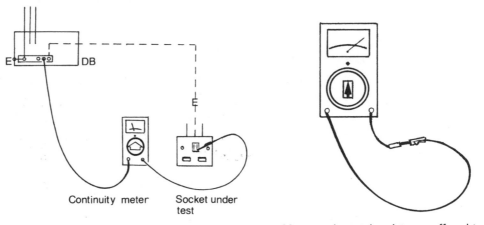

Continuity meter   Socket under
                          test

**Testing protective conductors
by use of a continuity meter.**

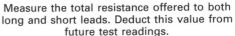

**Measure the total resistance offered to both
long and short leads. Deduct this value from
future test readings.**

The total resistance of the test leads must be measured before testing the current protective conductor serving each switch, ceiling outlet, socket and other electrical accessories. This is simply done by joining the two test leads together. The value obtained must be deducted from future test readings and the correct value of the current protective conductor in **ohms** will then be obtained.

The resistance of a conductor
The internal resistance of a conductor of electricity is directly proportional to **length** but inversely proportional to **cross-sectional area**. Therefore, the further the continuity tests are made from the distribution centre, the greater will be the resistance value of the protective conductor. This is made more apparent when each conductor is the same size.

How it is done
Start near to the distribution centre and test the current protective conductor serving each electrical accessory in the installation. Tests must also be made on independently routed conductors that serve water pipes, sink units, air ducting, etc. Always disconnect independently routed conductors before testing is carried out. This will provide an exact value.

High continuity values
Higher than expected continuity values must be treated with suspicion and the cause investigated at once.

The problem is often caused by one or more of the following:

- Contaminated connections
- Loose connections
- Connections not made
- Site broken connections
- Severed cable (by others)
- Conductor severed by overtightening

It is important to ensure that all current protective and bonding conductors linked to other conductive parts not necessarily to do with the installation are sound and electrically secure before an installation is commissioned.

When testing is complete, check the continuity meter by joining its leads together and if necessary readjust the instrument pointer to **zero** using the adjustment screw below the display panel.

| Exercise 2.15 | *Continuity testing* |

1. Why is it necessary to measure the total resistance (in ohms) of the instrument's test leads before continuity testing is carried out? Answer in the space below.

2. For this practical exercise you will need to carry out continuity tests on a simulated electrical installation.

   (a) Demonstrate that you are able to use a continuity tester or a multimeter set to the ohms scale for the purpose of continuity testing.
   (b) Use the table below provided to record all values obtained from the current protective conductors serving the simulated electrical installation.
   (c) Any defects or high continuity values must be traced and rectified.
   (d) Explain to your assessor your progress through each principal stage of testing.

Circuit no.	Name of circuit	True value of the protective conductor in ohms
1.		
2.		
3.		
4.		
5.		

Domestic lighting arrangements

Domestic lighting circuits are wired from the **point of distribution**. This will take the form of either a traditional **fuseboard** or miniature circuit breaker distribution centre. Such an installation would be carried out using either 1.00 mm^2 or 1.5 mm^2 PVC-insulated and sheathed cable. Industrial lighting schemes are wired using single insulated PVC-insulated cables drawn through welded steel conduit or box trunking.

The basic circuitry required when installing a one-way (that is, switched from one position only) lighting circuit is shown here. The practical arrangements will be dealt with later.

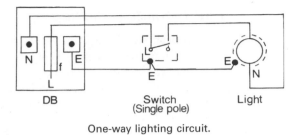

One-way lighting circuit.

Polarity of switches

The **polarity** of a conductor is whether it is **positive** or **negative**. A switch installed to control a lighting arrangement must always be supplied with a positive or **live** conductor. This will stop any danger of electrical shock from the lampholder when the switch is in the 'OFF' position. The black neutral conductor should never be wired to a switch that will either make or break one conductor (this type of switching action is known as a **single pole switch**). If this were to happen the live conductor would still be present at the lampholder even when the switch was in the 'OFF' position.

Two-way switching

Two-way lighting systems are wired in an entirely different fashion from the familiar one-way arrangement and this can be carried out using the joint box method. In practice, the switching arrangement is wired using two- and three-core PVC-insulated and sheathed cables.

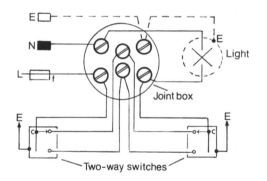

A two-way lighting circuit using the joint box method.

An alternative technique

An alternative technique used to wire a two-way switch without the use of a traditional six-terminal joint box is shown here. This system is sometimes known as the **conversion method**; it has the advantage of having all cable terminations accessible from one level and is often much quicker to install.

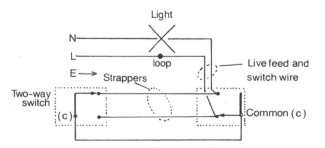

A basic one-way lighting circuit converted to a two-way arrangement.
The existing single-way switch is replaced with a two-way switch,
and another two-way switch is added in circuit elsewhere.

Intermediate switching

Intermediate switching is only used with a two-way lighting system. It is a method of control when three or more switches are required to serve a lighting arrangement. There are no constraints on the number of intermediate switches that may be used. Wiring is carried out using a three-core with earth lighting grade cable. Only the **yellow** and **blue** conductors are used. The two **red** conductors are joined together inside the switch box by passing the switching action completely.

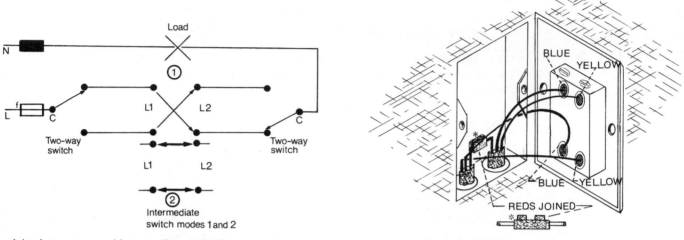

A basic two-way and intermediate switching arrangement.

Practical wiring: intermediate switching.

Types of switches

Domestic switches are designed to switch either one or many lighting arrangements. In summary, switches can be obtained as follows:

1. Single gang (the name given to a stand-a-lone switch)

    - One-way
    - Two-way
    - Intermediate
    - Double pole (meaning that both **live** and **neutral** conductors are switched together)
    - Dimmer; one-way and two-way
    - Sensi-touch
    - Ceiling pullcord switches; one-way and two-way
    - Time lag; mechanical diaphragm type and electronic type
    - Passive infra-red wall switches
    - Key switches (switches that are operated with a simple key)

2. Double gang (two identical switches side-by-side in the same plastic moulding)

    - Two-way
    - Dimmer; both either one-way or two-way
    - Sensi-touch; one-way switching

3. Three gang

    - Two-way; all switches are identical

4. Four gang

    - Two-way; all switches are identical

5. Six gang

    - Two-way; all switches are identical

6. Eight, nine, 12, 18, and 24 gang

These are **modular switching assemblies** supplied in component form comprising:

- A steel switch box
- Switches or indicator lamps, blanking-off components, fuse units, push-button switches, miniature flex-outlets, etc.
- Switch mounting **yokes** (sometimes known as **grids**)
- Multi-gang switch decorative face plate

This type of modular design allows many different types of miniature accessories to be used and is a helpful ally when designing a large installation.

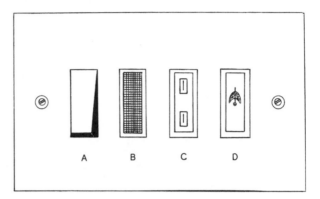

A four-gang modular switch. A = one-way switch;
B = indicator lamp; C = key switch; D = mains operated bell push.

Final power circuits

Final ring circuit

Socket outlets, designed to serve domestic or industrial installations are usually wired in the form of a **final ring circuit**. Formerly called a **ring main**, this method of power distribution has many advantages over the more traditional methods of wiring. Unlike the single socket served from a single fuse (a method popular before the mid-1950s) a final ring circuit can serve an unlimited number of sockets, provided certain conditions are met.

These involve the size and type of cable to be used for the area to be served with sockets. Also, the type of **overcurrent protection** (fuse, circuit breakers, etc.) needed to serve the installation is important.

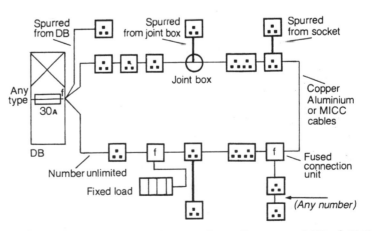

Final ring circuit recommended for a maximum floor area of 100 m². PVC-,
rubber-insulated or mineral-insulated cables may be used. Conductor size:
copper = 2.5 mm²; aluminium = 4.0 mm²; mineral-insulated = 1.5 mm².

Spurred socket outlets

A **spurred** socket is a socket that is wired from the final ring circuit. The spur may be supplied from a **mainline final ring socket**, a **joint box** or a **fused connection unit**. Only one spurred socket is permitted per socket in the final ring circuit. For example, if twenty 13 amp socket outlets have been installed to form the main installation, an additional 20 may be added to the circuit in the form of spurred sockets. Spurred sockets are always wired using one twin with earth PVC-insulated and sheathed cable.

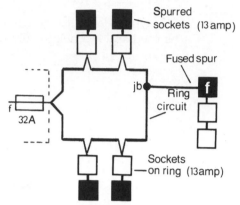

One unfused spur may be wired from each main line socket outlet.
jb = joint box; f = fuse or circuit breaker.

There is an exception to this rule:

*An unlimited number of sockets may be installed as a spur from the final ring circuit providing the sockets are supplied by means of a **fused connection unit**.*

This point is illustrated here and shows that only a maximum of 13 amps may be drawn from this spurred section of the final ring circuit as it is protected by means of a 13 amp fuse.

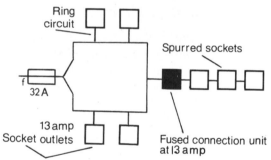

An unlimited number of 13 amp socket outlets may be served by a fused connection unit. This type of wiring accessory is sometimes known as a **fused spur**.

Wiring

Wiring is carried out using PVC-insulated and sheathed cable in domestic installations. The cable is either clipped on the surface or hidden in the fabric of the building. When concealed under the plaster line it is usual to place plastic or **steel channelling** (sometimes called **capping**) over the cables as a means of protection and future rewiring.

At the fuseboard

The basic components of a typical fuseboard are shown here. The multiway terminal bar shown as 'A', which is separated from both **phase** and **neutral** live conductive parts, accommodates the **current protective conductors** sleeved with green/yellow PVC oversleeving. The earthing bar, as it it often known, is usually marked with a

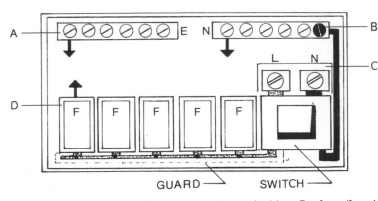

Basic fuseboard showing components: A = earth terminal bar; F = fuses/fuse holders; B = neutral terminal bar; L = live input terminal; N = neutral input terminal.

British Standard 3939 earth symbol.

letter 'E' or a BS 3939 symbol as shown here. The two heavy terminals (labelled 'C') at the top of the switch are reserved for the incoming supply conductors: the live on the left and the neutral on the right. The neutral terminal distribution block, labelled 'B', serves all outgoing circuits. Conductors must be ranged in the same order as the outgoing phase conductors so that the neutral wires can be immediately targeted. The protected red phase conductor is terminated at the top of the **fuse holder** 'D'. Each individual circuit must be terminated into its own fuse or circuit breaker. Heavy current-consuming circuits are placed nearest the main control switch, while lighter loads are ranged furthest from the switch. Circuit destinations are written in the spaces provided.

Radial circuit

The radial circuit is an acceptable alternative to the final ring circuit when the maximum demand for current is small. Advantages stem mainly from cheaper installation costs in both time and material. The basic requirements for a radial circuit serving a floor area of approximately 50 m^2 and the requirements when the area to be served is up to 20 m^2 are both shown here. In the latter case, the cable size is reduced from 4.0 mm^2 to 2.5 mm^2 when PVC-insulated and sheathed cables are used.

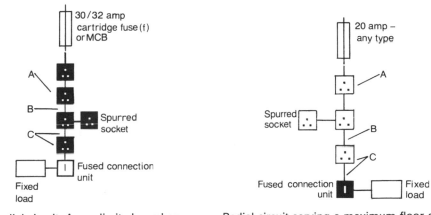

Radial circuit. A = unlimited number of 13 amp socket outlets; B = cable size: PVC- or rubber-insulated – 4 mm^2, aluminium conductors – 6 mm^2, mineral-insulated cable – 2.5 mm^2; C = maximum floor area of 50 m^2.

Radial circuit serving a maximum floor area of 20 m^2. A = an unlimited number of 13 amp socket outlets; B = cable size: PVC- or rubber-insulated – 2.5 mm^2, aluminium conductors – 4 mm^2, mineral-insulated cable – 2.5 mm^2; C = floor area.

Domestic final circuits

There are many different final circuits that may be installed. They are all wired in a similar way, but the cable size and the rating of the overcurrent protection device (fuse, miniature circuit breaker, etc.) are different.

The table below lists fifteen common circuits and shows which size of cable and the rating of the overcurrent protection device that will be expected when PVC-insulated and sheathed cable is laid in the following conditions:

- Routed away from thermal insulation
- A stand-alone cable not grouped with others
- In an ambient temperature of no more than 20°C
- When the protective device is a miniature circuit breaker.

Circuit	Size of conductor (mm²)	Rating of protective overcurrent device (amps)
Final ring circuit (ring main)	2 × 2.5	30 or 32
Gas-fired central heating	1.0 or 1.5	5 or 6
Cooker	6.0 or 10*	30, 32 or 40*
Electrically heated shower	6.0 or 10*	30, 32 or 40*
Mains operated door bell	1.0	2.5, 5 or 6
Fixed wall heater	2.5	15 or 16
Garage sub-main	4.0 or 6.0*	16 or 32*
Immersion heater (3.0 kW)	2.5	15 or 16
Off-peak heating	2.5	16 or 20
General lighting	1.0 or 1.5	5 or 6
Bathroom shaver point	1.0	2.5 or 6
Extractor fan	1.0	2.5 or 6
Television amplifier unit	1.0	2.5 or 6
Dedicated circuit for computer	2.5	20
Smoke alarm	1.0	2.5 or 6

Electrical correction factors for **grouping**, **ambient temperature thermal insulation**, and the use of **semi-enclosed fuses** have not been applied.

*Note: figures with asterisks are connected; for example, 6 mm² conductor would have a rating 30 or 32 amps, but a 10 mm² conductor would have a rating of 40 amps.

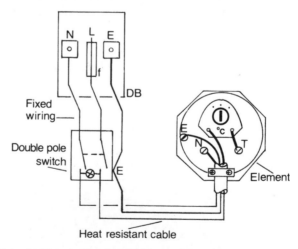

A typical immersion heater circuit. DB = distribution board.

Steel accessory boxes

Steel accessory boxes are used to accommodate and protect the accessory from mechanical damage or contamination.

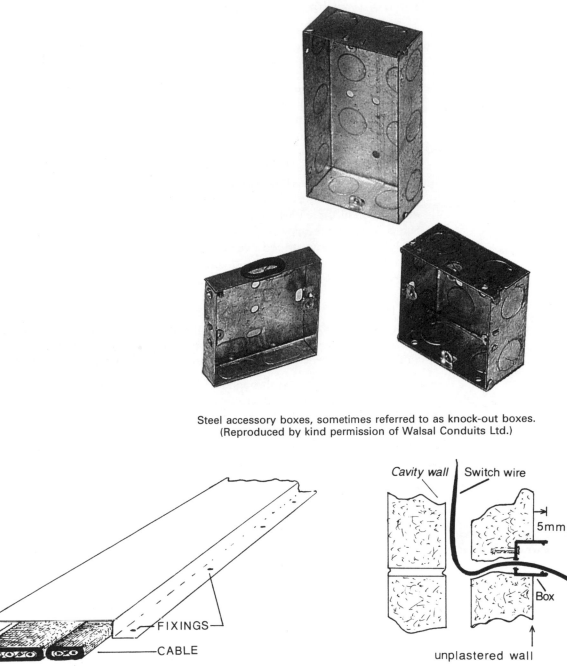

Steel accessory boxes, sometimes referred to as knock-out boxes.
(Reproduced by kind permission of Walsal Conduits Ltd.)

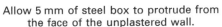

Steel or PVC channelling for domestic cabling.

Allow 5 mm of steel box to protrude from
the face of the unplastered wall.

When the installation is to be hidden under the plaster line, cables must be neatly laid and capped with steel or PVC channelling. Holes to accommodate accessory boxes need to be carefully made, making sure that the box is not placed too far back into the wall. This is to avoid using long machine fixing screws when mounting the accessory. Ideally allow 5 mm to protrude from the face of the unplastered wall so that the finished plaster line is reasonably flush with the leading edge of the box. Use wood screws and expansion wall plugs to fit the steel box into the recessed wall. Never use nails! Square boxes are usually manufactured with three fixed tapped lugs and one adjustable lug. Use the adjustable lug to gain alignment when the accessory is fitted. Always fit **rubber grommets** in the holes of the steel boxes after the pre-cut '**knock-outs**' have been removed. This will protect the cable sheath from sharp steel edges.

After the wall has been plastered

When plastering has been completed and is dry, remove any contamination from the inside of the steel accessory box and neatly trim any overhanging plaster. Retap the threaded fixing lugs and carry out the following:

1. Remove the outer sheath of the cable using a pair of sharp **side cutters** to split the end of the cable. Pull the two halves of the sheath until approximately 4–5 mm from the rubber grommet.
2. Cut the conductors to suit the position of the terminals but leave sufficient slack.
3. Remove about 10 mm of insulation from each conductor using a pair of wire strippers. Never use side cutters for fear of nicking the copper conductor.
4. Lightly twist together all **common** conductors and place them in the correct terminal housing; the red phase conductor serves terminal 'L' and the black neutral conductor serves terminal 'N'.
5. Screw home the terminal screws.
6. Add a green/yellow striped oversleeve to protect and identify the bare copper current protective conductor and connect into the terminal marked 'E'.
7. Screw the accessory to the steel box using the machine screws provided.

Flying leads

Green/yellow insulated flying leads fitted from the back of the steel accessory box to the earth terminal serving the accessory need only be fitted in the following circumstances. Reference is made to **Regulation 543–02–07**:

- If the installation is wired through steel trunking and the trunking system is acting as a current protective conductor.
- When the installation or circuit is wired in mineral-insulated cable.
- When the circuit is drawn through steel conduit.
- If the circuit has been wired using PVC/steel wire armoured PVC-insulated cable.
- When both threaded lugs serving a steel accessory box are adjustable.

When a flying lead is used, the cross-sectional area must be at least equal to that of the current protective conductor serving the sheathed cable used for the accessory.

Exercise 2.16

Domestic lighting and power

1. In the space below, complete and name the wiring diagram shown here.
The wiring arrangement shown below is:

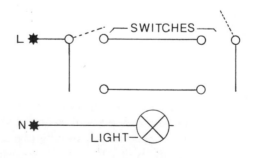

2. What type of lighting switch should be used when several switches are to be grouped together? Write your answer in the space below.

3. A green/yellow insulated flying lead attached from a steel accessory box to an accessories earth terminal must be fitted in which of the following circumstances?

(a) When the installation is wired using PVC-insulated and sheathed cable
(b) When both threaded lugs serving an accessory are adjustable
(c) When the installation is wired using steel conduit
(d) When the installation is wired using PVC-u conduit

(e) When the installation is wired using mineral-insulated cable

(f) On any installation using mains voltages

4. For this practical exercise you will require the following:

- 2 two-way surface mounted lighting switches
- 1 six-terminal lighting joint box
- Three core with earth PVC-insulated and sheathed cable (either 1.0 or 1.5 mm^2 in cross-sectional area)
- Appropriate cable clips and fixing screws
- A wooden assignment/work-board
- Approximately 400 mm green/yellow PVC oversleeving
- A surface mounted batten holder (lighting fitting)
- A suitable power source
- A lamp suitable for the power source and the batten holder

(a) Demonstrate to your assessor that you are competent to wire and commission a two-way lighting circuit using the **joint box** method.

(b) Ensure that all bare conductors are mechanically secure and correctly located.

(c) Observe polarity. Test for continuity, insulation and polarity.

(d) Components must be safely secured without damage to the installation.

(e) Check that the circuit is correct before commissioning.

(f) Extra low voltage should be used for this practical exercise. (**Do not dismantle this exercise yet.**)

5. For this exercise you will require the following:

- Three surface mounted 13 amp sockets
- A quantity of twin plus earth 2.5 mm^2 PVC-insulated and sheathed cable and tools to suit
- Suitable cable clips, wall plugs and fixing screws
- A small quantity of green/yellow PVC oversleeving
- A small distribution board with a 30 or 32 amp overcurrent protection device

(a) Demonstrate to your assessor that you are competent to wire and commission a small final ring circuit of which one socket will be a spur from one of the ring circuit sockets.

(b) Connect the installation to a suitable overcurrent protection device inside a distribution centre.

(c) Test for insulation, polarity and continuity values.

(d) Ensure that all conductors are correctly sleeved or colour coded and that there is no strain on the terminations. Check that there is a suitable amount of slack cable left at the sockets.

(e) For this exercise, site-simulated conditions would be preferable.

6. For this exercise you will return to **exercise 4** above.
The following will be required:

- One surface mounted intermediate switch
- Fixing screws and cable clips
- Side cutters, wire strippers, small and medium screwdrivers
- Three core with earth, lighting grade cable
- One 5 amp connector
- Green/yellow oversleeving

(a) Demonstrate to your assessor that you are able to incorporate an intermediate switch in the two-way lighting circuit you installed as **exercise 4**.

(b) Check that the circuit is working as designed.

(c) Check that there is a suitable amount of slack cable left at all switches and that all conductors are properly sleeved, colour coded and correctly terminated.

(d) Test for polarity and insulation and continuity values.

Joint boxes and their uses

Joint boxes give freedom of access to cable installations and are used for the following three purposes:

1. As a method of spurring off supply circuits to remote locations.
2. For interconnections when lighting and power arrangements are installed.
3. As a practical method to terminate or cap a redundant live cable.

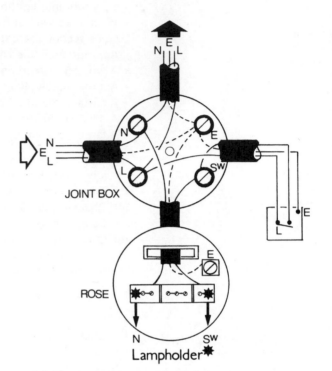

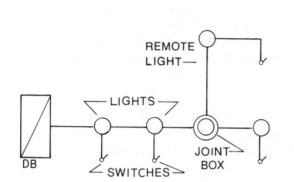

Junction boxes can be used as a method of spurring off circuits to remote locations. DB = distribution board.

Joint boxes may be used for lighting arrangements; a one-way lighting circuit is shown here.

The **central joint box system** is an alternative to the '**loop-in**' method when wiring lighting arrangements. Briefly, a PVC-insulated and sheathed lighting cable is routed from a local fuseboard or distribution centre to serve an insulated adaptable box. The box, usually made from PVC-u, is approximately 100 mm square and 25 mm in depth. The supply cable is terminated into a block of 15 amp connectors, which is secured to the base of the box. Additional circuits, together with switching cables, are added to the system and terminated in the connectors provided.

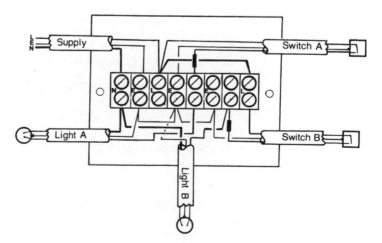

Lighting installation: central joint box method.

Advantages and disadvantages

Advantages

One of the advantages of this arrangement is that all interconnections are made inside the central joint box. This is a simple method of connecting as long as all cables are identified by marking. If cabling is installed unmarked, a great deal of time is wasted in re-establishing the role of each cable.

Another advantage is that only one cable is used to serve a lighting or switch point. Cable crowding, as experienced with the loop-in method, is eliminated. Other advantages stem from the fact that the majority of cabling is connected during the first fix or wiring stage of the installation when it is quicker to connect exposed cabling.

Disadvantages

The disadvantages of using joint boxes may be summarised as follows:

- Floor traps must be installed above the joint box
- Not practical if a **chipboard** flooring has been laid
- Practical access to the joint box is necessary
- Only practical in roof spaces if chipboard flooring is used

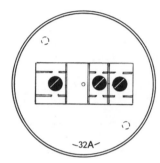

In power distribution junction boxes heaver cable terminals are used.

Power circuits

Joint boxes may be used as means of extending cabling serving power circuits or to provide suitable access points for testing and routing to remotely placed sockets or fused connection units. Always cut to length the conductors to be terminated.

Domestic joint boxes used for power distribution are rated either 30 or 32 amps and are fitted with three heavy terminals. Lighting grade joint boxes are rated at 20 amps and have either three, four or six terminals. Choice will depend on the requirements of the installation.

Exercise 2.17

Spurs from a joint box

1. In the space below, give two methods for wiring lighting arrangements other than the traditional loop-in method.

2. Give one advantage of using the central joint box method of wiring a lighting installation.

3. Why would it be impractical to use the joint box method of wiring in a house where chipboarding is to be used as flooring?

4. For this practical exercise you will require the following:

- One 30 or 32 amp joint box
- Two single surface 13 amp socket outlets
- Green/yellow oversleeving
- 2.5 mm² PVC-insulated and sheathed power cable
- Suitable cable clips
- $\frac{3}{4}$" or 1" × no. 8 wood-screws
- A work-board

(a) Demonstrate that you can competently use a power joint box as means of spurring a cable to serve a remotely sited socket.

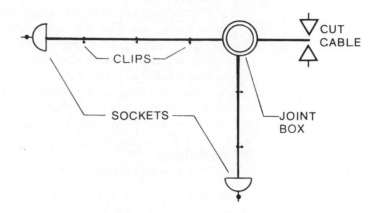

(b) Ensure that all conductors serving the joint box are cut to measure and that a suitable amount of slack cable is left at the sockets. Check that all terminations are correctly made. Test for polarity and insulation and continuity values.

Ceiling roses

A modern ceiling rose is constructed of three independent sections where conductors can be safely terminated.

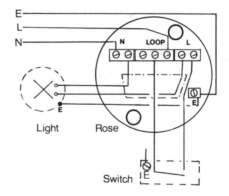

Ceiling roses are made with three independent sections.

The role played by each section is as follows:

- The left-hand section is reserved for the **neutral** supply conductors (in and out) and the neutral conductor serving the lamp holder.
- The middle section, divided into three, accommodates the permanent **live** conductors (in and out) and the red live conductor, which supplies the switch with electricity.
- The section ranged to the right, which is divided into two, provides termination for the **switch wire** and also the flexible conductor, which serves one side of the lamp holder.
  (The term **switch wire** is given to the conductor that becomes **live** when the switch has been placed in the 'ON' position. It is usually **black**, colour coded **red**).

The cable supplying electricity is terminated as shown here. The black neutral conductor is terminated into the left-hand side of the terminal block, while the live red conductor is terminated into the middle section.

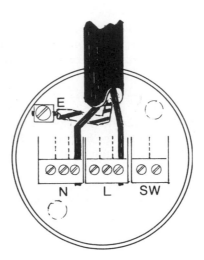

The supply or 'feed' cable is terminated as illustrated. E = earth
(the current protective conductor); L = live; N = neutral; SW = switch wire.

Wiring to the control switch

A separate cable is routed from the ceiling rose to serve the switch where both
conductors and the bare current protective conductor are terminated. The black
switch wire must be colour coded at the switch and at the ceiling rose when using
PVC-insulated and sheathed cable. The status of the conductor is now clearly seen to
have been altered. Use either red plastic oversleeving or PVC-adhesive tape. See
Regulation Table 51A.

Wiring at the ceiling rose

When the cable on route to the switch has been stripped of its outer sheathing at
the ceiling rose, the red '**switch – feed**' conductor is placed with the incoming live
supply conductor in the middle section. The black (colour coded red) switch wire is
then placed to the right of the middle section next to the flexible conductor serving
one side of the lamp holder.
Never switch the neutral conductor.

Two plate method

A lighting installation may be carried out using the two outermost terminal sections
serving a modern ceiling rose and a standard six-terminal lighting joint box, as shown
here. The advantage of this system is that the majority of cables may be laid and
connected during the first fix stage of the installation. It then becomes far quicker and
easier to connect the second fix electrical accessories as there are only a few cables
present.

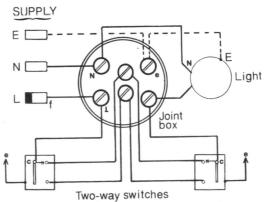

Lighting installation – joint box method. This illustration shows
a two-way lighting arrangement using a six-terminal junction box.

The disadvantage is that it can be very difficult to trace and identify faults at a later stage, especially if chipboard has replaced the original floorboarding present when the installation was commissioned.

Batten holder

The difference between a pendant drop (often called a ceiling rose and lampholder) and a modern **batten holder** can be seen here. Batten holders are installed where ceilings are low or if there is a need for a lighting accessory to be placed on the wall. This type of fitting is obtainable in a straight or angled format. The terminal arrangement is comparable to that of a modern ceiling rose; wiring is carried out in the same way as employed for a modern ceiling rose.

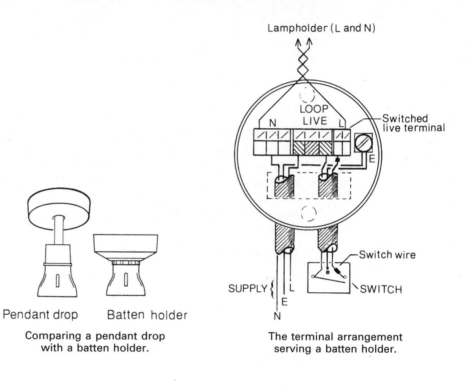

Comparing a pendant drop with a batten holder.

The terminal arrangement serving a batten holder.

Exercise 2.18 *Lighting circuits*

1. Referring to the figure illustrating the base of a typical ceiling rose (below), draw the route taken by the permanently live conductor and the neutral conductor to their respective terminals. Draw a continuous line to represent the permanently live conductor and a dotted line to represent the neutral conductor.

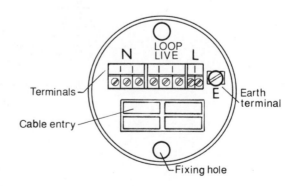

2. Why is it considered necessary to colour code the black 'switch-wire' at the switch position and the ceiling rose?

3. State briefly, in the space provided, the role batten holders play in electrical installation work.

4. For this practical exercise you will require the following:

- One batten holder and a small distribution board
- An extra-low voltage supply
- An extra-low voltage lamp to fit the batten holder
- A surface mounted one-way switch
- Lighting cable and suitable cable clips
- Green/yellow PVC oversleeving and red PVC oversleeving
- A wooden work-board
- Fixing screws and hand tools

(a) Demonstrate to your assessor that you are competent to wire a batten holder controlled by a single pole one-way switch.
(b) Use the figure on p. 150 as a guide for this practical exercise.
(c) Test using an extra-low voltage supply.
(d) Check your polarity throughout the installation.
(e) Check that all components are safely secured without damage being done to the insulation.
(f) Ensure that the circuit has suitable overcurrent protection.
(g) Test for polarity and continuity and insulation values.

Protection against short circuit and overcurrent conditions

Short circuit

The definition of a short circuit is when two current-carrying conductors of opposite potential, such as a **live** and a **neutral** conductor serving a socket outlet, accidentally touch each other. This will cause the circuit fuse element (the overcurrent protection device) to blow apart violently.

Overcurrent

Overcurrent may be defined as a current flowing in a circuit, the amount of which exceeds the rating of the fuse, miniature circuit breaker or cable rating. Unlike a short circuit condition, an overcurrent can develop in an electrically sound circuit.

Overcurrent devices

The common overcurrent devices used in electrical engineering are listed in the following table.

Device	Application and comments
Fuse (semi-enclosed)	Used in low-cost electrical installation work. Easy to detect when the fuse element has ruptured. The wrong sized fuse wire could be fitted.
Small cartridge fuse (to BS 1361)	Fitted to 13 amp plugs to protect the flexible service cable.
High breaking capacity fuse (HBC)	These fuses are large cartridge fuses and are fitted into purpose made fuse holders. They will tolerate heavy circuit current interruptions.
Miniature circuit breaker (MCB)	Used in commercial and industrial installations and increasingly in domestic installations. Looking like a switch, it is easy to see when an overcurrent condition has occurred as the device will automatically switch to the 'OFF' position. Expensive compared with semi-enclosed fuses.
Moulded case circuit breaker (MCCB)	Used to protect supply cables serving distribution centres. Similar but larger than miniature circuit breakers. Able to withstand greater current flow and short circuit conditions. Generally coloured brown. Not used for the protection of final circuits.

Exercise 2.19 *Overcurrent devices*

1. Cartridge fuses to BS 1361 are usually used when heavy currents are experienced within a circuit. State in the space below whether this statement is true or false.

2. Short circuit conditions will only appear in an electrically sound circuit. State in the space below whether this statement is true or false.

3. For this practical exercise your tutor will provide five reference-marked overcurrent devices/components.

   (a) Demonstrate to your assessor that you are able to distinguish between these five types of overcurrent protection devices.

       1. semi-enclosed fuse
       2. small cartridge fuse
       3. high breaking capacity fuse (HBC)
       4. miniature circuit breaker (MCB)
       5. moulded case circuit breaker (MCCB)

   (b) Record your findings in the table provided.

Component reference number	Name of component
1.	
2.	
3.	
4.	
5.	

4. For this practical exercise you will need to take a close look at the distribution centre that serves the electrical installation in your home, or that of a friend.

(a) Sketch in the blank space provided the general outline of one of the overcurrent protection devices serving a circuit in your own home. State the type that has been installed.

(b) Note the the maximum current rating in amps of the device and the circuit which it controls.

(c) Record these observations in the space provided.

(d) Remember that this distribution centre is **live**. Do not tamper with any of the component parts or conductors!

Overcurrent device installed:

Current rating in amps:

Name of circuit:

Cable supports

Installation specifications are often strictly enforced on large construction sites. Fixings and **cable carriers**, such as conduit, trunking and cable tray, must be installed precisely in accordance with the written specifications. Safe and approved methods to meet these requirements should be used at all times, making sure that the finished work is neat and tidy to harmonise with the site instructions. Routing of cable supports must be clear of other services.

Eleven different cable or **supplementary cable supports**, together with the material used in their construction and their uses in electrical engineering, are listed below.

Cable support	Material used in construction	Application
Brackets (site assembled)	Mild steel, painted with a protective coat	Cable tray or steel trunking installations
Cable clips	PVC-u	Securing surface mounted PVC-insulated and sheathed cable
Cable saddles and fixing strap	Plain copper or aluminium – plastic coated	Used for fixing surface mounted mineral insulated cables
Cable ties	Nylon, nylon-reinforced, stainless steel, and PVC	Applied to bunched cables for support and retainment

HEAD   RATCHET   TAIL

Channel support	Mild steel, various finishes, e.g. PVC-u, and glass reinforced polyester	Used in conjunction with a purpose designed nut attached to a spiral spring. Channel support is used to accommodate cable trunking, cable ladder or cable tray
Cable cleats	PVC-u, polythene, glass-reinforced nylon, aluminium alloy or stainless steel	A chunky wrap-around support used for fixing steel wire armoured cables and other specialised cables. Used mainly in industry but also has many commercial applications
Pipe hooks (sometimes referred to as crampets)	Steel: galvanised or black stove enamelled finish	For fixing conduit to soft building fabric before plastering is carried out. The pipe hook is hammered into the brickwork directly over the conduit to provide support

A pipe hook is used to secure conduit to wall, which is to be plastered. A = impact area for knocking the fixing device into the wall; B = hooked section for securing the conduit.

Cable support	Material used in construction	Application
Saddles	Steel: galvanised or black stove enamelled finish. Also in PVC-u	Fitted over surface conduit installations to provide support for the pipe work. Available in many different sizes
Self-adhesive cable clips	Plastic-coated mild steel	Suitable for light-weight extra-low voltage cables routed along walls or within electrical cabinates Self-adhesive cable clips. A = protective plastic membrane, which can be peeled from the back of the clip; B = adhesive backing; C = soft steel or alloy cable-fixing device.
Strapping	Galvanised mild steel or reinforced nylon	A multi-holed cable strap often used to group and support armoured cables in cable ducts Galvanised cable strapping.
Racking support	Mild steel: various finishes to suit conditions	Purpose made brackets and fixing devices for supporting heavy-duty cable ladder, trunking or cable tray. Mainly used for industrial applications. Ideal when several runs of cable tray are required to be grouped together where wall space is limited or rationed

Cable supports: fixing difficulties

When positioning and fixing difficulties are experienced during an installation that specifies defined routes and methods to use, an approved alternative remedy must be sought with an appropriate person. On large construction sites it is often the responsibility of the resident electrical engineer to determine alternative methods of installation. Smaller sites rarely have this luxury and cable support methods or problems are usually left to the **site agent** or **building contracts manager** to find a solution.

| Exercise 2.20 | *Cable supports* |

1. In the space below, state whether the following is true or false:
PVC-u cable clips fitted with masonry nails are used to support surface mounted mineral-insulated grouped cable runs.

2. Describe briefly in the space below how cable ties can be used in an installation.

3. Name which cable support could be used for routing extra-low voltage circuits in a roof space.

4. For this practical exercise the following components will be required:

- Two metres of PVC-insulated and sheathed power cable
- Two metres of PVC-insulated and sheathed lighting cable
- Cable clips to suit the size of cable
- Two metres of **2L1.5** or **2L2.5** PVC-sheathed mineral-insulated cable (MI)
- MI cable clips to suit the cable chosen

(a) Demonstrate to your assessor that you are competent to clip two common sizes of PVC-insulated and sheathed cable with PVC cable clips. Smooth out and straighten the cable then clip every 120 mm.
(b) Repeat this exercise using mineral-insulated cable and the cable clips provided. Do not test.

This practical exercise is best carried out in a controlled, simulated work situation.

5. For this practical exercise you will require the following:

- A selection of PVC-insulated single cables, which can be grouped together
- Several suitable cable ties

(a) Using PVC or nylon cable ties, show how grouped cables can be supported on their route.
(b) Place the cable ties every 70 mm. Once wrapped around the grouped cables and firmly in position, the cable tie should be cut as near to its head as possible. Mount the cables on a suitable cable tray.

British Standards

An organisation known as the **British Standards Institution** lays down minimum standards and stipulations for a wide selection of components, consumer goods, and graphical symbols, etc. The Institution is usually referred to as the BSI and the standards are identified by the letters 'BS' followed by numbers, e.g. BS 5378 Graphical Safety Signs.

The following table shows a selection of British Standards titles relating to electrical engineering. A copy of these standards can be obtained direct from the BSI, or may be seen in large public reference libraries. BSI standards are usually produced on red anti-reprographic paper, which does not allow the printed text and symbols to be photocopied.

BS specification number	Subject matter
BS 88	Cartridge fuses (voltages up to 1 kilovolt AC).
BS 1362	Cartridge fuses used in conjunction with 13 amp plugs.
BS 1363	Switched and unswitched socket outlets. Plugs rated at 13 amps.
BS 1710	Identification of pipelines (colour coding).
BS 1852	Alphanumerically coded resistors used in electronics.
BS 3036	Semi-enclosed (rewirable) fuses up to 100 amps at 230 volts.
BS 3871	Miniature and moulded case circuit breakers.
BS 3939	Graphical symbols used for electrical and electronic drawings.
BS 4293	Residual current operated circuit breakers (RCD).
BS 4941	Starters for electric motors up to 1 kilovolt AC.
BS 5266	Emergency lighting.
BS 5378	Graphical safety signs.
BS 5467	Armoured cables with thermosetting insulation.
BS 5733	General requirements for electrical accessories.
BS 5839	Fire detection and alarm systems in buildings.
BS 6004	PVC-insulated cables for electric power and lighting.
BS 6207	Mineral-insulated cables (MI).
BS 6977	Insulated flexible cables for flexible connections.
BS 7671	IEE *Wiring Regulations*.

Examples of graphical British Standards – safety signs

From 1 January 1986 it became a legal requirement that all safety signs must comply with British Standard 5378 Part 1. This ruling resulted from a European Community directive in 1977 and the Safety Signs Regulations of 1980.

The British Standard divides safety signs into four groups:

Group 1   WARNING, of which there are 19
Group 2   PROHIBITION, of which there are eight
Group 3   MANDATORY, of which there are 14
Group 4   EMERGENCY/SAFE CONDITION, of which there are seven

Some of the safety signs which meet the requirements of BS 5378, Parts 1 and 3, are shown here, together with a selection of graphical location symbols used in electrical drawings to BS 3939.

A selection of safety signs meeting the requirements of BS 5378 Parts 1 and 3.

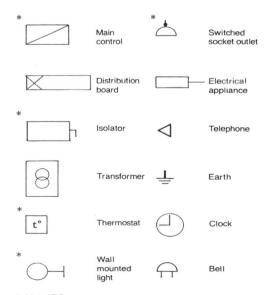

* Not IEC

Graphical location symbols used in electrical and electronic drawings to BS 3939.
IEC = International Electrotechnical Commission.

Exercise 2.21	*Safety signs*

For this practical exercise you will require permission to access your college or place of learning.

(a) Locate, sketch and identify one warning sign for each catagory of BS 5378 Part 1 Safety Signs.

(b) Use the form provided below. As an example, a specimen sign has been provided.

Sketch of the warning sign	Location of the warning sign	Meaning of the sign
		Harmful substance.

Sketch of the prohibitory sign	Location of the prohibitory sign	Meaning of the sign

Sketch of the mandatory sign	Location of the mandatory sign	Meaning of the sign

Sketch of the emergency/safe condition sign	Location of the emergency/safe condition sign	Meaning of the sign

Chapter 3

Basic electronic assembly and wiring

Exercise		Page	Date	Signed by Trainer
3.1	Insulated component boards	162		
3.2	Wires and conductors used in electronics	164		
3.3	Plugs, sockets and connectors	166		
3.4	Resistors and graphical symbols	169		
3.5	Electronic components	173		
3.6	Identifying the values of electronic components	175		
3.7	Electronic drawings	179		
3.8	Measuring resistance, current and voltage	185		
3.9	Soldering electronic components to make a circuit	190		
3.10	Assembling an electronic circuit	195		
All information presented in this section is complete, accurate and legible				
All information presented in this section is in the format required				
The trainee observes statutory regulations at all times				
The trainee implements safe operating practice and always demonstrates regard for the safety of others				

Insulated component boards

The three types are as follows:

1. Printed circuit boards

An example of a printed circuit board (PCB).

2. Bread board
3. Strip board

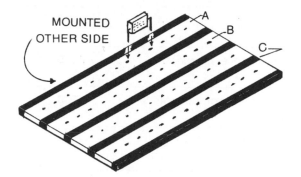

Strip board. A = copper strip or track; B = holes for soldering components;
C = insulation between the tracks

Printed circuit boards

Made from glass reinforced plastic, printed circuit boards (PCB) are built for the
requirements of the circuit. Conductive paths are printed onto the surface of the
insulating material at the manufacturing stage. Each electronic device is mounted on
the side opposite the conductive path by first drilling tiny holes through the printed
circuit to accommodate the components, and then soldering them.

Surface mount technology
This method of assembling electronic components is similar to the traditional PCB,
except that holes are made during the manufacturing process. The components used
are known as **surface mount devices** (SMD).

All types of printed circuit boards are usually provided with an '**as-fitted**'
component layout diagram. This enables easier assembly work and virtually eliminates
wiring errors as the diagram is printed with values on the reverse side of the circuit
board.

Bread board

Bread boarding is often used in the development, experimental and proving stages of
a project. This technique has several advantages compared with the traditional printed
circuit board and strip board methods. These advantages are:

- It is quicker to install the components
- No soldering is required
- Far fewer connections are needed between components
- All components may be dismantled and reused
- Design changes are easy to carry out
- Fewer tools and equipment are required

Construction

A typical bread board is shown here. Components such as transistors, resistors, capacitors and connecting wires are linked together by placing them into holes that have spring retaining contacts. Some holes are internally joined together, providing means for a common connection inside the bread board. All rows are labelled with letters and numbers.

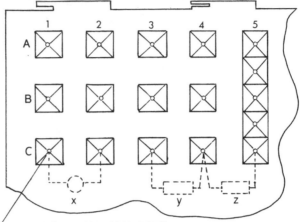

Bread board. Components 'x', 'y' and 'z' are connected via the insulated side of the bread board.

Strip board

Strip board may be used for production work but more often is employed for prototype assembly schemes. A typical strip board is made from plastic reinforced glass fibre. Running its entire length are uniform strips of copper with holes called **tracks**. The reverse side has a totally insulated surface on which to mount components. Once placed into position they are soldered permanently onto the copper strips via the holes, which have been factory drilled into the insulated board.

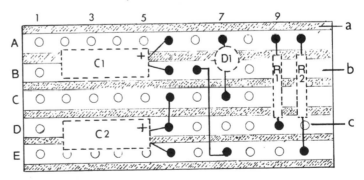

Strip board. a = insulated board; b = copper strip, or sometimes referred to as track; c = component connection holes (components are placed on the totally insulated side of the strip board and soldered onto the copper track on the other side); R1 and R2 = resistors; C1 and C2 = capacitors; D1 = diode.

Isolating components

If it is necessary to isolate components, breaks can be made in the copper track. This can be done simply by twisting a drill bit of a suitable size by hand into the chosen hole. The two halves of the track will then be isolated from each other.

| Exercise 3.1 | *Insulated component boards* |

1. State in the space below whether this sentence is true or false.
Bread board components can be assembled without the need for soldering.

2. When work is carried out using strip board technology how can two components that share the same copper track be isolated from each other?

3. For this practical exercise the following will be required:
- A small section of strip board
- Three resistors, each of a manageable size
- A soldering station
- Multi-core solder

Demonstrate to your assessor that you can mount the resistors onto the strip board in the following practical arrangement:

(a) Any two resistors in **parallel** formation
(b) The third resistor placed in series formation with the other two resistors as illustrated here

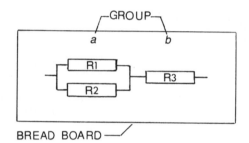

(c) Solder all three resistors to the bread board using soldering techniques mastered in Chapter 2

Use heat shunts to avoid thermal damage to the components if considered necessary. Component leads should be correctly tinned. Joints must be electrically and mechanically sound, free from excessive flux and solder, and bright in appearance. Dull and pitted solder and solder spikes will not be allowed.

4. For this exercise you will require the following:

- A small section of bread board
- Three resistors of your choice

(a) Demonstrate to your assessor that you are able to arrange the three resistors in a similar fashion to that shown on p. 161. In the illustration, Resistor 'X' is connected to C1 and C2. Resistor 'Y' is connected to C3 and C4, while Resistor 'Z' is connected to terminals C4 and C5.
(b) Demonstrate that all components are mechanically sound within the housing of the bread board.

Wires and cabling

The following table shows a selection of cables and, where applicable, their approximate current-carrying capacity or capacitance generated per metre. Many of these cables have tinned conductors to prevent oxidisation occurring.

Cable	Description/application	Current rating or capacitance generated per metre
Miniature screened cable (twin)	Seven strands of 0.2 mm^2 tinned copper, insulated with PVC and protected by a braided screen sheath covered with a coloured outer sheath. The cores are twisted for audio 'hum' reduction. May be obtained as a single core cable. Available in many sizes. Used in audio amplifiers, video recorders, radio and television receivers, computers and in data transmission installations. Reproduced by kind permission of RS Components Ltd.	Capacitance 120 pF from conductor to conductor; 210 pF from the conductor to the braided screen sheath.
Ribbon cable Reproduced by kind permission of RS Components Ltd.	Ribbon cable is produced as a flat arrangement of flexible cables in many sizes. Not intended as power cable. Used in personal computers and as data links to printers. The conductors are individually insulated from each other and are often colour coded. Conductors are formed from stranded tinned copper and are laminated between a layer of PVC film.	Capacitance between 45 and 55 pF between cores. Very low current rating.
Co-axial cable	Manufactured with a bare copper single conductor or a bare copper stranded conductor; cellular polythene insulated. A copper screening braid is placed over the insulation and the cable is sheathed with PVC. Used for television aerial down leads and low level signal circuits. S I C SHEATH I = insulation/dielectric; C = inner conductor; S = screen/outer conductor.	Capacitance between 50 and 100 pF.
Signal cable Reproduced by kind permission of RS Components Ltd.	Each conductor is formed from seven strands of tinned copper wire 0.22 mm^2, PVC insulated. Each cable conductor is coloured, usually red, blue, yellow and black and is protected by a moulded outer PVC sheath. This type of cable is used for low voltage, low current electronic work.	Each core is rated at approximately 1 amp per core. Working voltage up to 60 volts AC.

Exercise 3.2

Wires and conductors used in electronics

For this practical exercise you will be given four numbered samples of different types of cable used in electronic work.

(a) Demonstrate to your assessor that you can correctly identify them and describe how each may be used.

(b) Record your answers in the table provided for you.

Cable no.	Cable	Description	Use
1.			
2.			
3.			
4.			

Plugs, sockets and connectors

There are many types of plugs, sockets and connectors, which are available for use in electronic engineering.

Definitions

Plug
This is a hand-held device with electrical contact pins designed to be slotted into a socket. A plug is usually attached to a flexible cable.

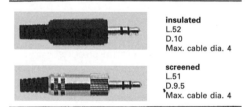

insulated
L.52
D.10
Max. cable dia. 4

screened
L.51
D.9.5
Max. cable dia. 4

Electronic three-pole plug.
(Reproduced by kind permission of RS Components Ltd.)

Socket
This is a device with internal contacts forming an elongated hollow or slot. These are called **female contacts** and are designed to hold a plug to serve electronic circuits.

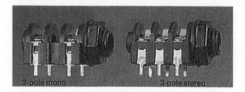

Two- and three-pole printed circuit board mounting sockets.
(Reproduced by kind permission of RS Components Ltd.)

Connector

This is a mechanical coupler, which has contacts known as **female contacts** and is used for joining conductors. See p. 164.

Types of plugs and connectors

The table lists six common plugs or connecting devices used in everyday electronics and describes their uses.

Accessory	Comments
DIN connector	DIN stands for **Deutsch Industrie Norm**. These plugs are used for television, tape recorders, amplifiers, audio equipment, computers and radio-receivers; they are available in 3, 4, 5, and 7 pins. The wired connections are soldered. The connection pins are often silver plated. Suitable for use up to 100 volts AC (150 volts DC) at 2 amps. 3-WAYS-5 END — VIEWS — SIDE
Speaker plugs	These are designed as two-pinned plugs; often one pin is flat while the other is round so that the plug can always be connected correctly. Used in audio-speaker circuits. Cable Moulded body Contact pins
Phono connectors	A squat type of plug often with a coloured insulated moulded body. Used in audio equipment. One insulated wire is connected to each plug. Can also be obtained as a moulded metal case type for heavier applications. Contact pin — Moulded body ⊢—— 33 mm ——⊣
Insulation deformity connectors	Often known as IDC connectors. Similar to telephone outlet connectors. The wires are not soldered or mechanically clamped; the insulation is ruptured when forced into the connector by use of an IDC connector tool. Often used to terminate **ribbon cable**. WIRE SOLDERED JOINT

Accessory	Comments
Banana plug	Usually 4 mm in width. Has a spring attached to the conductive part. Will accept one soldered connection only. Often used to serve certain types of test instrument leads.
Co-axial plug	Commonly used to terminate television aerial cables. Used also with video equipment. Made from aluminium but a PVC-moulded case type can also be obtained. Designed to accept one co-axial cable only.

Each plug is polarised, which means that it is impossible to reverse. Each pin has its own particular role, for example, positive, negative, earth, switch wire, control wire, etc.

| Exercise 3.3 | *Plugs, sockets and connectors* |

1. Insulated deformity connectors are often used to terminate ribbon cable. What other uses do they have?

2. Why are the contact pins serving a **speaker plug** shaped differently?

3. State whether the following statements are true or false in the spaces below.

   (a) Banana plugs are often used to serve instrument test leads.
   (b) Coaxial plugs are used to serve high-voltage equipment.
   (c) Phono connectors are used for telephone installations.

   (a) True/false   (b) True/false   (c) True/false

4. For this practical exercise you will be given seven different types of plugs or sockets, which have been numbered.

   (a) Correctly identify each type of component and briefly describe its common use. Write your comments in the space provided.
   (b) Use the blank table provided to fill in relevant information.

Component no.	Name of component	Application
1.		
2.		
3.		
4.		
5.		
6.		
7.		

Electronic components

Resistors

The table below describes four different type of resistors used in everyday electronic engineering. The use and BS 3939 location symbol of each resistor is also given.

Type	Description/use	BS 3939 symbol	Illustration (current rating in proportion to the size of the component)
Fixed resistors	Made from carbon, metal oxide, metal film or metal glaze. Values from 10 ohms to 1 000 000 ohms. Power rating from 0.125 W to 300 W, aluminium housed with a heat sink.		
Sensing resistors	These are called **thermistors** and are used for sensing temperature differences. At low temperatures, the device has a low resistance but will rapidly increase in value at higher temperatures.		
Slider resistors	A dual carbon track used for direct wiring or printed circuit board mounting. Made as a **log** or **linear** resistance track. Values between 10 and 100 000 ohms.		
Variable resistors	A circular resistor, wire wound or carbon track. Used in radio, television receivers, and audio equipment. Made as a linear resistance track. Values from 10 to 1 000 000 ohms. Power rating up to 3 W. Can be selected with an internal switch independent of the resistance track.		

Many other types of resistor are available including the following:

- Conductive plastic
- Open (skeleton) preset
- Sub-miniature
- Thick film resistor networks
- Top adjusting
- Wire wound

Remember that resistors can be colour coded or alphanumerically coded (see p. 22).

Problems associated with resistors

Like any other electrical component, resistors will sometimes break down. They will then be left in an **open circuit condition** (a resistor that will not allow the passage of electricity) or their resistance value will increase so much that problems will occur in the circuit. This is often caused by water or moisture.

Capacitors

See text on p. 24.

Graphical symbols: electronics

The graphical location symbols shown in the table below are used to illustrate and present details of electronic circuitry. All symbols can be used with each other and can be included in BS 3939 line diagrams.

Fuse		Variable resistor		Slow release relay coil	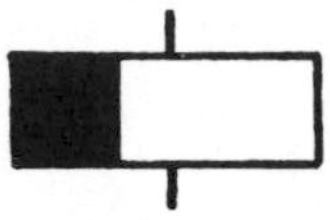
Conductor		Voltage divider	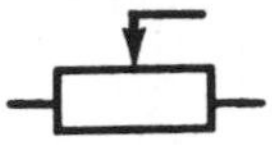	Filament lamp	
Flexible conductor		Triode valve	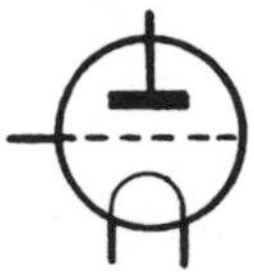	Diode	
Junction of conductor(s)		Linear motor	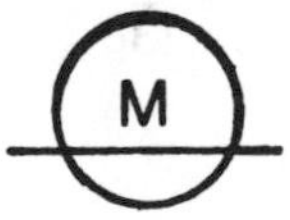	Zener diode	
Screening of conductor(s)		Capacitor		Light emitting diode	
Earth		Electrolytic capacitor		Thyristor	
Clean earth		Bidirectional diode varistor		Transistor (pnp)	
Signal lamp		Inductor with core	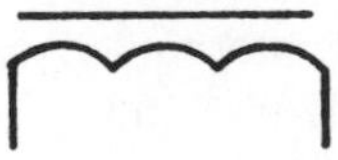	Siren	
Fixed resistor		Transformer	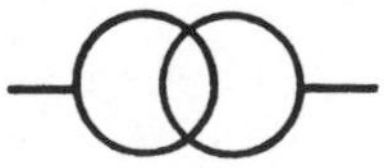	Bell	

Draw the symbols sharing a circuit in similar proportions to each other if practical. For example, it would be difficult to draw the thyristor and varistor, shown here, on a similar scale to the other components as there is so much detail present.

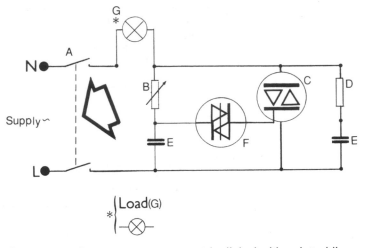

Components that operate as one must be linked with a dotted line.
This illustration shows the wiring arrangement for a domestic dimmer switch.
A = double pole switch linked with a dotted line; B = variable resistor;
C = varistor; D = resistor; E = capacitor; F = thyristor; G = lighting load.

Components that operate in unison (together and as one), such as the double pole switch drawn as Item 'A' in the figure, must be linked with a dotted line.

Never design your own location symbols as this will cause confusion to others. Only use those recommended by **British Standards**.

Exercise 3.4

Resistors and graphical symbols

1. From knowledge gained, label the component parts in the illustration provided.

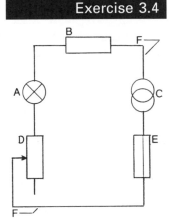

(a) Suggest a title for this illustration.
An appropriate title would be:

(b) Use the table below to record your results.

Components in labelled form	Name of component
Component A	
Component B	
Component C	
Component D	
Component E	
Component F	

2. For this practical exercise you will be given four different types of resistor as listed in Part (b) of this question.

(a) Demonstrate to your assessor that you are able to identify all four of these resistors.

(b) Suggest a practical use for each resistor.

(c) Write your comments in the table provided for you.

Type of resistor	Use	Brief discription of the shape of the resistor (conformation)
1. Variable		
2. Slider		
3. Sensing		
4. Fixed		

Other components and accessories

Static sensitive devices (SSDs)

As metal oxide semi-conductor components are sensitive to static electricity of more than 100 volts, care must be taken when they are handled.

Static electricity can be generated by wearing a nylon shirt or by walking across certain types of carpet while wearing synthetic rubber-soled shoes. It can become a nuisance when working with static sensitive devices.

Combating static electricity

The following methods can be used to help reduce the risk of damage when handling SSDs:

- The use of **anti-static handling devices** to prevent fingers touching the lead conductors.
- Handle only the ceramic part of the packaging and never remove SSDs while live in circuit.
- Special areas can be set aside where **floor** and **bench mats** are made electrically common with each other and also to an electrical earth point. Engineers wear a wrist strap, which is electrically earthed. These areas are often known as **special handling areas** where all tools and technical aids are electrically earthed.

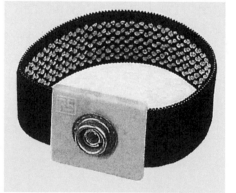

Elasticated anti-static wrist strap.
(Reproduced by kind permission of RS Components Ltd.)

Complementary metal oxide semi-conductors (C-MOS)

C-MOS components are made using complementary metal oxide semi-conductor technology. They have a wide supply voltage range and, together with low power consumption and high noise immunity, they are extremely versatile. However, C-MOS devices must be handled with care and stored wisely to prevent static electricity from damaging the component parts.

C-MOS semi-conductor devices include:

- General integrated circuits (ic)
- Memory integrated circuits
- Crystal oscillator modules
- Operational amplifiers
- Programmable clock/timer integrated circuits

This list gives some indication of the range available. All these devices must be handled carefully so they do not become damaged.

Discrete semi-conductor devices

This is a term given to diodes, thyristors, triacs or any stand-alone electronic device that is not part of an intergrated circuit.

TTL devices

TTL stands for **transistor transistor logic**. This type of electronic component belongs to a group that also contains the complementary metal oxide semi-conductor. Each group member provides the same basic logic functions but is designed with different supply voltages, circuit layouts, switching speeds and logic levels. Data sheets are needed giving details of pin connections; these are obtainable from the retail/wholesale outlet where the component was purchased.

Transistor-transistor-logic circuit (TTL), 74LS series.
(Reproduced by kind permission of RS Components Ltd.)

Metal can and flat pack electronic components

Metal can

This is a hermetically sealed relay (a switch operated by a coil of wire, which, when energised, opens or closes electrical contacts) enclosed in a metal container as shown here.

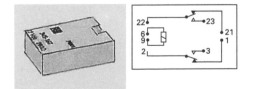

Metal can relay.
(Reproduced by kind permission of RS Components Ltd.)

Flat pack

This type of component is a double pole changeover relay for low current usage (typically 2–4 amps AC or DC), so-called because of its low profile.

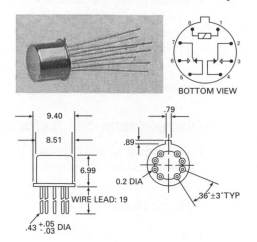

Flat pack – a low profile double pole changeover relay.
(Reproduced by kind permission of RS Components Ltd.)

Plastic dual-in-line (DIL) and 'D' type connectors

Dual-in-line sockets.
(Reproduced by kind permission of RS Components Ltd.)

DIL connectors

Dual-in-line plugs are designed to terminate ribbon cable or single conductors, and to be fitted into standard integrated circuit sockets. Insulation displacement connections are housed in the plug to allow the ribbon cable to be terminated. This provides a permanent connection for each conductor serving the ribbon cable.

This type of in-line connector can be found serving computers and printers, etc.

An integrated circuit socket can be selected for soldering directly into a printed circuit board as the illustration shows.

'D' type connectors

Looking like the tall Roman capital letter D, this type of connector is used to terminate ribbon cable. There are three methods of termination:

15 way 'D' type connectors.
(Reproduced by kind permission of RS Components Ltd.)

1. Insulation displacement method providing a four-point contact.

View of IDC termination

An insulation displacement connector (IDC) shown in its most basic form.
(Reproduced by kind permission of RS Components Ltd.)

2. Traditional soldering method.
3. Crimp snap-in contacts aided by an insertion/extraction tool. Contacts are placed in a 'D' type **insulated plug shell** at the rear of the insulation. When the conductors have been fitted, an integral locking mechanism is used to make sure that the connection is mechanically and electrically secure. This type of connector is used to serve computers and printers, etc., and is obtainable with 9–50 **termination points** (these termination points are called **ways**).

Exercise 3.5   *Electronic components*

1. Using your own words, describe in the space below a method of preventing damage to sensitive electronic components from static electricity.

2. Describe, using your own words in the space provided, the contents of a flat pack.

3. This practical exercise is designed to test the student's ability to correctly identify electronic components.

   You will be given nine numbered electronic components or products associated with the electronics industry as listed:

   • An anti-static product
   • A 'D' type connector or plug
   • A four-point insulation displacement connector
   • A dual-in-line connector
   • A metal can relay
   • A flat pack changeover switch
   • A 1 watt carbon resistor
   • A C-MOS integrated circuit
   • A capacitor

   (a) Demonstrate to your assessor that you are able to identify **six** of the listed items and state their uses.
   (b) Write down your answers in the table provided.

Component/ product no.	Name of component or product	Typical use
1.		
2.		
3.		
4.		
5.		
6.		

Identifying components and their values

Electronic components can be easily identified by the following:

- **Colour coding**: resistors, capacitors, wires and cables, etc.
- **Component leads**: capacitors, resistors, transistors, etc.
- **Shape of component**: flat packs, metal can relays, capacitors, semi-conductors and integrated circuits, etc.

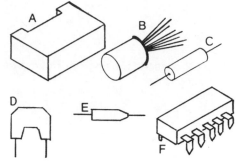

Many components can be identified by their shape: A = flat pack; B = metal can relay;
C = resistor; D = capacitor; E = diode; F = integrated circuit.

- **Relative position or arrangement of the leads**: diodes, TTL devices, relay bases, etc.
- **Electrical mains voltage colour coding for flexible conductors**: brown: phase; blue: neutral; and green/yellow: current protective conductor
- **The material from which the component's outer case is made**: metal used for variable voltage regulators or metal can relays; plastic used for TTL devices and other integrated circuits; colour translucent plastic used for light emitting diodes, tubular glass fuses, etc.

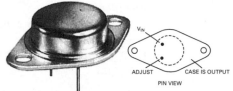

Three-terminal variable voltage regulator.
(Reproduced by kind permission of RS Components Ltd.)

- **By alphanumerical means**: letters and numbers printed on some types of resistors
- **By observation**: reading types, values and tolerances, etc.

Discrete semi-conductor devices

This is a term given to any **separate stand-alone electronic component** that is not an integrated circuit. Examples are: transistors, diodes, thyristors, triacs and thermionic valves, etc. Thermionic valves are used for radio, television and other high-frequency transmissions.

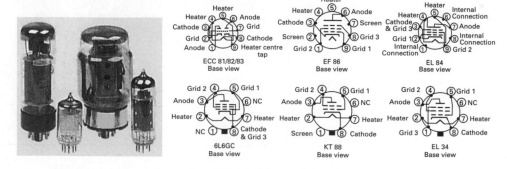

Thermionic valves. (Reproduced by kind permission of RS Components Ltd.)

Universal counter using extra-low voltage C-MOS technology. (Reproduced by kind permission of RS Components Ltd.)

Integrated circuits, such as clock timers, universal counters and line drivers and receivers (integrated circuits designed for data transmission), are not classed as discrete semi-conductors.

Reference data

Reference data for electronic components and products can be obtained from the following sources:

- Manufacturer's component and **product catalogues**
- Manufacturer's component **data sheets** (These give technical details, facts and figures and examples of application to ensure that components are correctly used.)
- **Colleges and public libraries** (Facts, figures and component details may be found in textbooks.)
- **Data libraries** (These store data sheets in a logical sequence.)
- **Data CD-ROM** (This is a compact disc software package designed for computers. CD-ROM stands for Compact Disc – Read Only Memory.)
- **Cellular data cards** (These cards are designed for use with a mobile phone and mobile computer.)
- **Data cartridges** (These are for filing information and may be used as a computer-disc back-up.)
- **Optical disks** (These are for data storage and information that requires change or updates.)
- Recordable **CD-R** (This has a high data storage capacity. It is able to store data such as graphs, text, audio information and video data.)

The purpose of these data banks is to provide readily accessible technical information for the user.

Exercise 3.6

Identifying the values of electronic components

1. Some electronic components can be recognised by the position or arrangement of their leads. In the space below, name two examples.

2. Give two examples of how components may be recognised by the use of colours.

3. How could a flat pack be readily identified from a metal can relay in poor lighting conditions?

4. Name three convenient methods of gaining access to technical information concerning electronic components.

5. This is a practical exercise to test your ability to identify electronic components by their shape, colour coding or the way in which their leads are arranged.
   You will be given six numbered components, all of which will be different in both shape and size from each other. All components will be known to you.

(a) Demonstrate to your assessor that you are able to identify all six of the components offered to you by their shape size, colour coding or lead arrangement.

(b) Write down your findings in the table provided.

Component no.	Component	How did you recognise the component?
1.		
2.		
3.		
4.		
5.		
6.		

6. Using a reference data source of your choice, find and record in the table provided, information about the following:

1. The lowest value 1 watt **carbon film** resistor currently manufactured.
2. The highest value 1 watt **carbon film** resistor currently manufactured.
3. The tolerance values offered for the highest value resistor chosen.
4. The length of the leads in millimetres serving the lowest value resistor researched.

Lowest value of carbon resistor researched and the length of the leads in millimetres		mm
Highest value carbon resistor researched and the tolerance values offered as a percentage		%
Source of information		

Electronic drawings

Circuit diagrams

Electronic circuit diagrams use symbols to represent parts such as resistors and capacitors and to show how they are connected with each other. Wiring is shown as vertical or horizontal lines, while the symbols drawn are those advised by **British Standard 3939**.

Information about INPUT is placed towards the left of a diagram. For example, in the figure here, the input is shown as tiny pieces of burnt matter resulting from fire that starts an alarm. Information about OUTPUT is put at the right of the diagram and is seen here as two centre terminals, which provide a **signal current** to a fire detection and alarm panel.

Custom-made electronic symbols should always be labelled.

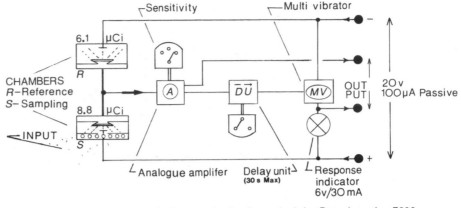

Smoke detector circuit diagram: ionisation principle. Based on the *F600* developed by CERBERUS of Switzerland.

Wiring diagrams

Electronic wiring diagrams are very detailed. They show the actual **point-to-point** wiring that has to be carried out and the interconnections that have to be made to produce a working circuit. Values are shown on all diagrams.

Wiring diagrams come in all shapes and sizes; a simple light-operated transistor switch working from a 9 volt battery supply is shown here.

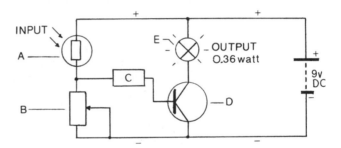

This wiring diagram illustrates a light-operated transistor switch. A = photo cell; B = variable resistor; C = fixed value resistor; D = transistor; E = lighting load.

As with circuit diagrams, wiring is shown as ruled lines. Positive conductors are always towards the top of the diagram, with the negative wiring towards the bottom. Wherever possible, **BS 3939** symbols should be used. Alternative symbols must always be clearly labelled, as should values and component numbers. Draw all input components to the left of the page and output components to the right.

In the figure shown here, the input is given as a **light sensitive resistor** and the output is a low wattage indicator lamp. This system of presenting wiring diagrams is based on the **cause and effect** principle: cause is to the left and effect is to the right.

Component layout diagrams

Component layout diagrams are often known as **physical layout diagrams** and show in exact detail how the electronic components are assembled on a **printed circuit board** or **strip board**. Each component part is drawn, labelled and numbered simply, and scaled in proportion to relative size. For example, the diagram here shows where three electronic components are to be soldered onto a small strip board, and how all three components are presented as a layout diagram.

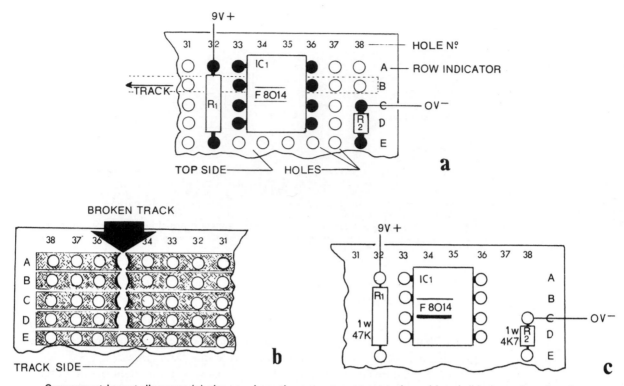

Component layout diagram: (a) shows where the components are to be soldered; (b) shows how breaks can be formed in the copper strip; and (c) shows the components presented as a layout diagram. (Holes have been enlarged to show the working concept more clearly.)

When mass produced products are to be sold, printed circuit boards are developed to enable the efficient assembly of components that make the finished product. During the development stages, component layout diagrams are drawn in a similar way to strip board assembly work diagrams.

A typical wiring diagram for an audio amplifier unit is shown here. Horizontal and vertical lines represent the interconnecting wiring, whereas electronic components are drawn to BS 3939.

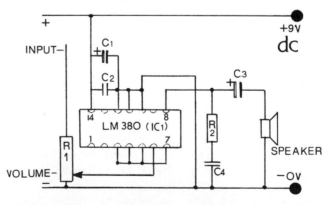

Audio amplifier. Horizontal and vertical lines represent the interconnecting wiring to the various electronic components.

This type of electronic drawing is essential when developing a prototype product. Often physical or component layout diagrams are printed on the top side of the strip boards as a guide for assembly. A board like this would look similar, in style only, to the figure shown here. If production numbers were to run into thousands, a manufacturer would use printed circuit boards for the product.

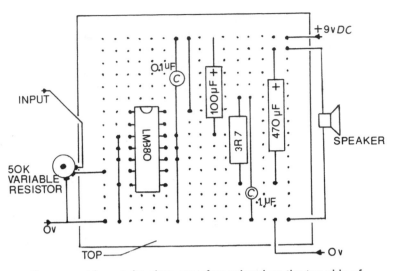

Component layout drawings are often printed on the top side of
strip boards as a guide for component assembly. This illustration
shows how components for an audio amplifier are placed.

| Exercise 3.7 | *Electronic drawings* |

1. Using your own words briefly describe the following:

(a) a circuit diagram
(b) a wiring diagram

2. What advantage can be gained by using a component layout diagram?

3. State the advantage of producing a printed circuit board (PCB) made especially for
the product (custom-made).

4. Draw, in the space below, a simple cause and effect **circuit diagram** of a bell push
controlling a combined bell and battery unit. Draw the components as circles,

squares or oblongs and the wiring as vertical or horizontal lines. Components should be labelled. BS symbols need not be used.

Instrumentation and electrical measurement: voltage, current, resistance

Electronics is dependent upon instrumentation so it is very important to know how to use the instruments properly. Refer back to Chapter 1 for details of instruments used in electronics, especially voltmeters, ammeters and ohm meters. The measurement of voltage, current and resistance will be reviewed here. It is essential that you understand these principles.

Measuring voltage

Voltage is measured in **parallel formation** with the circuit to be tested. This means that the value in volts is obtained by placing the insulated probes between both positive and negative live conductive parts.

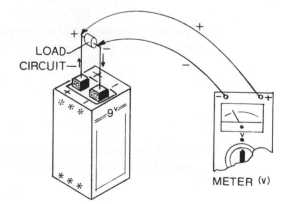

Voltage is always measured in parallel formation with the circuit to be tested.

To measure DC voltage safely use this step-by-step method:

1. Check that the instrument and the insulated probe leads are free from damage and are dry.
2. Place the red lead into the **positive terminal port** of the meter and the black lead into the '**common**' terminal port of the meter.
3. Switch to the direct current (DC) voltage range and if possible choose a suitable voltage to work with. If unsure which voltage to choose, it is wise to switch to the highest setting and work down.
4. Place the red positive probe into the positive live conductive part under test. Then place the black negative probe into the live negative conductive part under test.
5. After the two probes are firmly in place, the meter's liquid crystal display (LCD) will show the electrical potential difference (voltage) of the circuit. Some digital multimeters have an LCD analogue 'bar-graph' indicator which can be very helpful.

Measuring voltage may be done in a similar way using an analogue test meter. But instead of reading a value displayed on screen, measurement is found using a traditional scale and pointer.

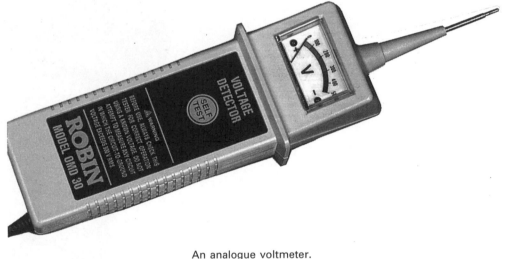

An analogue voltmeter.
(Reproduced by kind permission of Robin Electronics Ltd.)

Measuring current

Current flow is a stream of particles called electrons. To measure electron flow an **ammeter** must be used. There are many different types of ammeter; each used for a particular application.

- Micro-ammeter   (for measuring millionth parts of an amp)
- Milli-ammeter   (scaled in one-thousandth parts of an amp)
- Analogue and digital (for general use; site and workshop)
- Clamp meter   (for use when circuit separation would not be practical)

Current measurements may be taken two ways:

1. By placing the instrument in **series formation** with the circuit under test.
2. By use of a clamp meter.

Method 1
When using a multimeter to calculate the amount of current being used, the circuit has to be broken and the meter placed in series with the load.

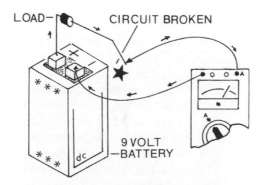

Measuring current flow using a multimeter placed
in series formation with the load.

To measure current safely, remember the following points:

1. Place the test probe leads into the correct safety terminal ports. There is often a choice of two: one to measure up to 200 milliamps and the other to measure higher current values up to 10 amps.

A digital multimeter, supplied with a heavy-duty
rubberised holster, being used as an ohm meter.
(Reproduced by kind permission of Robin Electronics Ltd.)

2. Switch off the electrical supply to the appliance under test. Next disconnect the live brown or red wire serving the appliance. Place one of the probe leads into the terminal that has just been disconnected. The other probe lead is then connected to the loose wire leading to the appliance.

3 Set the selector switch to **amps** and choose a suitable range. If in doubt, start from a higher range and work down.

4. Once the circuit is switched 'ON', the current value in amps can be seen on the meter's display panel.

Method 2

Measuring current drawn from a circuit by using a clamp meter is very simple. Most are designed for use on alternating current (AC), but direct current (DC) models are available. Digital clamp meters are auto-ranging and multi-sensing, which means that a selector switch is unnecessary. They are ideally suited for measuring stable loads, motor starting currents and other peak current and surges found in electrical work. The accuracy of this type of meter is about ±2% of the displayed value.

To test, open the **hooded insulated jaws** and place around the cable. The **electromagnetic induction** produced by the circuit will be collected by the jaws of the instrument. The induction will then be processed and shown as a readable current value in amps.

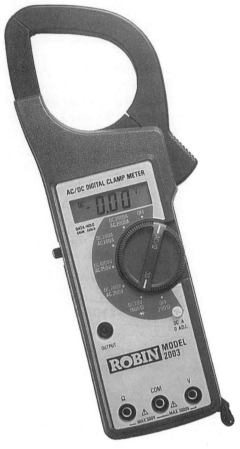

A clamp meter can be used to measure current flow through a conductor.
(Reproduced by kind permission of Robin Electronics Ltd.)

Measuring resistance

The resistance of a circuit is measured in ohms. It is simply a measure of a component's opposition to the flow of electricity.

There are many different types of ohm meter, each suitable for a particular use.

- Milliohm meter   (for measuring very low values)
- Stand-alone meter   (for specialised use)
- Multimeter ohm meter (for site and workshop use)

An ohm meter has its own source of electricity and does not rely on the circuit under test to provide energy.

Resistance must never be measured on a live circuit. Doing so could badly damage the test instrument.

To measure resistance safely, remember the following points:

1. Make sure that the circuit or component under test is completely isolated from the electrical supply.
2. Set the multimeter to the **ohms scale** and choose a suitable resistance range.
3. Place the black probe lead into the safety terminal port marked '**common**'. Then put the red probe firmly into the terminal port labelled ohms or Ω (the Greek letter omega).
4. Touch the probe tips together and check that either '000' appears on the meter's display panel or the instrument's pointer swings to the **zero** position.

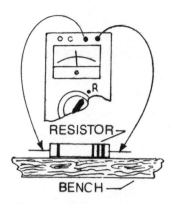

Bench testing a resistor with an analogue multimeter. (Illustration not to scale.)

5. If the zeroing check is satisfactory, resistance values can be taken. Test as though testing for voltage; place a probe either side of the workpiece under test. The pointer will show the value in ohms on the scale.

Wave-forms

Signal generators and **pulse generators** are used in the electronics industry to produce visual images of electrical signals. These images are called **wave-forms**.

On its own, a signal generator is not able to provide a visual image, so it is used together with an instrument called a **cathode-ray oscilloscope** (CRO).

An oscilloscope is based on the cathode-ray tube with a similar screen to a television, but much smaller. The screen provides visual images of one or more varying electrical quantities, which can be fed into it. All wave-form traces are time based.

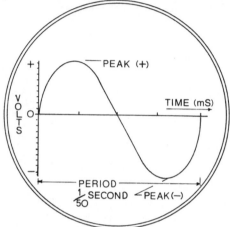

A typical sinical wave-form trace viewed from an oscilloscope.

Listed in random order below are the various types of wave-form that can be generated.

1. Sinical (as a sine wave)
2. Triangular
3. Saw toothed (source: pulse generator)
4. Squared
5. Pulsed (source: pulse generator)
6. Stepped (source: pulse generator)

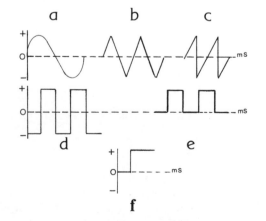

Various types of wave-form which can be generated. a = sine wave; b = triangular; c = saw tooth; d = square; e = pulse; f = step.

Always refer to the **operators' manual**, because similar instruments do not always operate in the same way.

| Exercise 3.8 | *Measuring resistance, current and voltage* |

1. What instrument is used to measure electron flow within a circuit?

2. State in the space below the practical advantage gained by using a clamp meter instead of a multimeter switched to the 'amps' scale?

3. Describe in your own words below what a milliohm meter is used for.

4. Why is it important to ensure that the electricity has been switched off before resistance values are taken?

5. Draw, in the space provided, three simple identical circuits comprising:

- One battery
- One switch
- One low valued resistor (the load)
- Connecting wire

Demonstrate by use of the sketches the following:

(a) how current may be measured;
(b) how voltage is measured;
(c) how the resistance of the load is taken.

6. For this practical exercise you will require the following:

- A battery or other extra-low voltage fused supply at 6 volts
- Insulated wire; 1.00 mm² would be ideal or 10/0.2 mm².
- A domestic lighting switch
- A suitable load (low value resistor; 3 ohms would be ideal)
- A multimeter

(a) Arrange the listed components to form a circuit as shown here.
(b) Demonstrate to your assessor that you are able to obtain values of **resistance**, **current**, and **voltage** using a **multimeter** from your arranged circuit. Select your components according to the layout of the drawing. Make sure that they are the correct value and type. Check that the circuit performs to specification or operation and put right any faults found before the circuit is switched on.

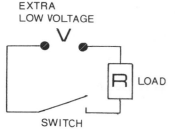

EXTRA LOW VOLTAGE

V

R LOAD

SWITCH

Common faults in circuit construction

There are many common faults that occur from time to time in electronic assembly work. Listed in random order below are some of the faults that may arise.

Resistor faults

Resistors that produce very high values may have been exposed to:

- Heat
- Moisture
- Movement of carbon granules
- Excess voltage

Circuit breaks

Open circuit (a break in the circuit) can be caused by:

- Mechanical failure
- Impurities within the component
- Mechanical stress
- Broken connections
- Broken resistance wire
- Bad manufacture
- Electrolytic/moisture action
- Separation/break-up of metal film
- Too much current
- Failure of soldered joints

Capacitor faults

- Plates shorting out: due to movement of silver in moist conditions (e.g. mica capacitors)
- Bloated: due to high temperature or moisture
- Short circuit: due to mechanical shock or rupture or too high a voltage
- Intermediate open circuit: due to mechanical damage
- Changeable values: fault condition between the dielectric (the insulation between the plates) and the capacitor plates

Handling, mounting and using electronic components

Handling components

Other than **static sensitive devices**, which will be dealt with later, electronic components need to be handled very carefully. Clean hands, patience and gentleness are required for electronic assembly work.

Always use a heat shunt (for example, a pair of long-nose pliers) when mounting semi-conductor components. Failure to do so could damage the device.

Mounting components

Components such as diodes, capacitors and transistors must be mounted and soldered with care. The following 16 practical points should be kept in mind when electronic assembly is carried out:

1. Any insulation serving a component at a point where soldering is to take place must be removed.
2. All parts to be assembled must be free from grease or any other form of contamination.
3. The removal of insulation should be carried out using purpose-made adjustable wire strippers.

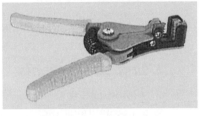

An automatic wire stripper will cut and
strip a range of wire sizes in one operation.
(Reproduced by kind permission of RS Components Ltd.)

4. Use **snipe-nose pliers** for the following tasks:
   - As a heat shunt (to protect the component from excess heat)
   - As a means of bending conductors
   - To set and mount component leads
   - When soldering components to circuit boards or terminal lugs, bend the leads of the components to keep them in place.

5. Mount the components properly. Check that the polarity is correct; that is, the positive lead to the positive terminal and the negative lead to the negative terminal. Examples of where the polarity must be correct are: batteries, diodes, polarised capacitors. Remember to use a heat shunt.
6. Most components and insulated linking wire may be directly mounted to the face of the circuit board.
7. Bend component leads at a slight angle. This will allow the component to be soldered without it falling out when the board is turned over.
8. Make sure that the soldering iron has the correct sized tips, is at its working temperature, is clean at the working end and is suitably tinned.
9. Clean the component leads to be soldered using a suitable **cleaning tool**. Tin as efficiently as possible without applying unnecessary heat as this could damage the component.
10. Place the component onto the circuit board using the method outlined earlier.
11. Apply the tinned soldering iron directly to the copper strip/component lead joint until it becomes hot enough to melt the solder to be used.
12. Maintain the heat to the joint and apply **rosin-core solder** directly to the area to be connected. Never over-apply or cause **splashing**. Too much solder could cause problems. Use a heat shunt when necessary.

SOLDER
SPLASH

—PCB

Solder splashes that spill over to adjacent copper
strips will cause electrical problems.

13. When the joint has cooled, snip off the unwanted section of the component lead as close to the joint as possible.

14. A well-made joint should have just the right amount of solder and should appear both bright and smooth without **spikes**. A small gap should be seen between the wire insulation and the soldered joint.

15. If the joint appears to be dull, spikey, have too much flux or is marked with minute hollows, it is best to resolder. If there is any doubt, use a milliohm meter to check the resistance across the jointed area.

16. Finally; check your work throughout for short circuits caused by solder splashes, solder spikes or loose strands of wire. Solder splashes may be removed using a **desoldering tool**. Ask your instructor to show you how it is used. Solder spikes can be eliminated by reheating the joint that is affected. Loose strands of wire can be quickly trimmed with sharp side cutters.

Using components

It is important to both use and handle components properly so care must be taken when assembling them on the circuit board. Some of the problems that may occur whenever electronic components are incorrectly fitted are given in random order in the table below.

Component	Common error	Consequences
Diode	Connected in reverse	In forward bias, this will stop current flow
Low wattage resistor	Placed where a higher power rating was required	Overheating/burn out
Polarised capacitor	Connected in reverse	Internal damage or explosion
Low working voltage capacitor	Placed where a higher working voltage component was required	Internal damage or explosion
Transistor	Incorrectly wired in circuit	Circuit malfunction
Metal oxide semi-conductors	Static voltages greater than 100 volts polluting the oxide insulating layer through incorrect handling	Damage caused to the oxide layer; component breakdown
Integrated circuits (IC)	Wrongly assembled	Breakdown in component and/or circuit
Transformer	Primary voltage connected to the secondary windings	Blown fuse or damage to both transformer and circuit

Static-sensitive devices

All **complementary metal oxide semi-conductors** (CMOS) are very sensitive to static electricity in excess of 100 volts, so great care must be taken when handling them.

Static electricity can be produced by wearing a nylon shirt or blouse or by walking across a synthetically produced carpet whilst wearing oil/heat-resisting rubber-soled shoes. This build-up of static electricity often becomes a source of annoyance in the electrical engineering industry. Placing a **neon test screwdriver** onto an electrical 'earth' every so often helps to overcome this problem.

Preventing static electricity

The following three methods can be used to help reduce the risk of damage to static-sensitive devices (SSD):

1. Workshop areas can be set aside where special floor and bench mats are used, electrically linked together and to an electrical earth point.

   Engineers working with SSD components are electrically earthed to the bench work-mat by using a suitable wrist strap and a light flexible cable. These areas are often know as **special handling areas** where all tools, soldering iron tips and other technical aids are electrically earthed.

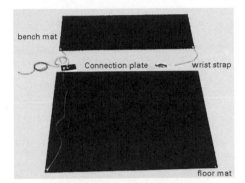

Antistatic work-station.
(Reproduced by kind permission of RS Components Ltd.)

2. The use of anti-static handling devices to prevent fingers from physically touching the lead wires of the SSD components.
3. By handling only the ceramic or plastic packaging and by never removing the static-sensitive device while live in circuit, or damage may occur.

Applying the correct voltage

It is important to check that the correct voltage is applied to the circuit board. An electronic project will fail if AC current is applied when DC is required. Similarly, the supply voltage must be correct for requirements or damage could be caused.

Additional points

The following points should also be noted:

- Make sure that components next to soldered joints are free from solder splashes.
- Check that all wires used for electronic work are of the correct type, size and colour coding.
- Wire just for the needs of the project. Too much wire can cause problems.
- Mount components so that their printed values are clearly visible.
- Use a heat shunt, snipe nose pliers or special purpose devices if there is any risk of damage to the delicate components when soldering is carried out.

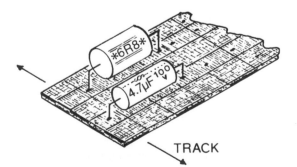

Component values must be clearly visible.

| Exercise 3.9 | *Soldering electronic components to make a circuit* |

1. List three common reasons why resistors malfunction.

2. Give two explanations why capacitors become bloated.

3. What can cause the value of a capacitor to be altered?

4. Why is it necessary to take note of polarity when connecting certain components?

5. Before soldering, how would you prevent a component from falling out of position from the underside of the circuit board?

6. Describe, using your own words, how a well-made soldered joint should look.

7. What would happen if a semi-conductor diode was placed the wrong way round in a circuit designed to illuminate an indicator lamp?

8. How can static electricity be generated?

9. Describe in your own words what is meant by the term **'special handling areas'**.

10. How would you reduce the risk of static electricity when handling static-sensitive devices?

11. For this practical exercise you will require the following:

   • A section of strip board and 60 mm of light gauge insulated wire
   • A small capacitor
   • One resistor
   • One small diode
   • Soldering iron and rosin-core solder

From knowledge gained, demonstrate that you are able to prepare and correctly handle electronic components before soldering takes place and that you are able to place them securely into position to prevent them from falling out when the strip board is turned over.

   Solder the components listed above onto the strip board as shown here. Avoid splattering solder, bridging adjacent tracks, solder spikes and dull joints.

   Identify each of the four components that you have soldered to the strip board to your assessor.

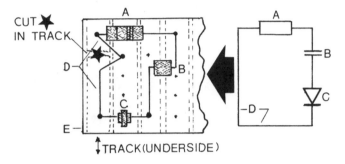

A = resistor; B = capacitor; C = diode; D = insulated wire; E = strip board.

12. For this exercise the following will be required:

   • A 9 volt battery
   • One light emitting diode (LED) at 10 milliamp
   • A section of strip board
   • A 1000 ohm low wattage resistor
   • Two terminal pins suitable for strip board work
   • A small switch (not for strip board mounting)
   • One battery terminal clip
   • 150 mm of light gauge red insulated wire (size: 7/0.2)
   • 150 mm of light gauge black insulated wire (size: 7/0.2)

Refer to the figure shown here and select the required components from your store. Check that they are of the correct type and value.

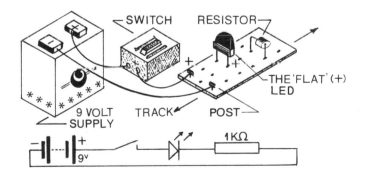

(a) Produce the circuit shown in the layout drawing by soldering the components to the strip board provided.
(b) Route the cables and fit the components in the correct position as shown in the diagram. Ensure that a small gap is present between the wire insulation and the soldered joint.

(c) Correct any errors before switching 'ON'.

(d) Demonstrate to your assessor that the circuit produced performs to specification.

(e) Unsolder the LED and resolder it to the strip board in the same place but in reverse. Switch on and show your assessor the event that followed.

Understanding electronic circuit diagrams

A simple circuit containing the following is shown here:

- A 3 volt battery
- A 10 milliamp diode
- A switch
- A low wattage indicator lamp
- A variable resistor
- Insulated connecting wire

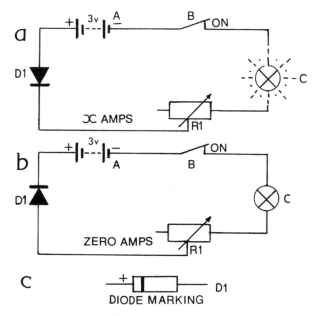

Forward and reverse biased circuit. A = 3 V battery; B = switch;
C = lamp; R1 = variable resistor; D1 = diode.

The wiring arrangement shown (in part (a)) is known as a **forward biased circuit**. If the variable resistor (R1) has its resistance removed by using a length of insulated wire to bridge either side of the component, the indicator lamp (C) will light up brightly when the circuit is switched 'ON'. When the semi-conductor diode (D1) is changed around (as shown in (b)), the indicator lamp will not light up. When in this reversed position the internal resistance of the diode becomes extremely high. This type of wiring arrangement (in part (b)) is known as a **reverse biased circuit**. Take care when wiring semi-conductor diodes in circuit. If more voltage is added to the circuit, a total breakdown of the diode can be expected.

From theory to practice

How the BS 3939 wiring diagram shown above may be applied to a typical strip board is shown here.

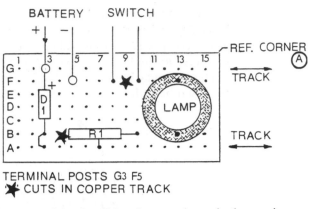

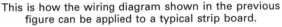

TERMINAL POSTS G3 F5
✭ CUTS IN COPPER TRACK

This is how the wiring diagram shown in the previous
figure can be applied to a typical strip board.

In order to isolate one section of circuit from another, the copper backing strip is
broken. This may be carried out using a **sharp knife** or a **drill-bit** slightly larger than
the diameter of the copper strip.

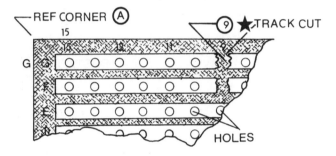

Isolating a section of strip board. (Seen from the under-side of the strip board).

Constructing a simple light-operated transistor switch

The wiring details serving a simple light-operated transistor switch shown here is the
same circuit as applied to a strip board. Here all the components are shown against
the backdrop of a circuit board. For clarity the copper conducting strips have been
drawn in full view. In practice they would be hidden from sight, being on the
underside of the circuit board.

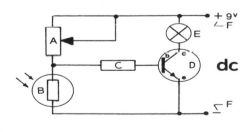

a

Constructing a light-operated switch.
A = variable resistor (100 kΩ);
B = light dependent resistor (ORP12);
C = resistor (2.2 kΩ); D = transistor (2N3053);
E = 6 V lamp at 60 milliamp; F = 9 V DC supply.

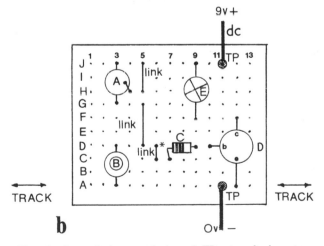

b

The circuit applied to a strip board. TP = terminal posts.
* Track cut

Light dependent resistors (LDR)

Light dependent resistors can be expensive, so it might be wise to solder flexible wires to the component before adding to the circuit. This way the leads need not be bent too close to the LDR and this will prevent them being from snapped off accidentally.

The best way to bend and prepare transistor leads for soldering to the circuit board is shown here. Bend component leads only once to reduce the risk of them snapping.

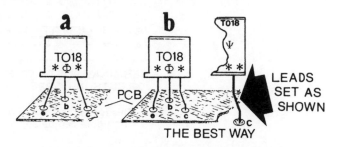

The prefered way to bend transistor leads for soldering:
(a) the wrong way; (b) the preferred way. b = Base; e = emmitter; c = collector.

Tapered terminal pins are used in assembly work for power (battery/transformer) input points.

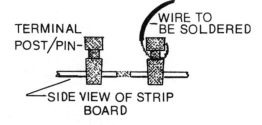

Tapered terminal pins/posts are used for power input/output points.

How your transistor works

A transistor may be compared to a workshop socket outlet. A small flick of the switch will permit a large amount of current to flow through the connected appliance. For example, a simple circuit can be designed to warn of the presence of moisture. When moisture is detected, a tiny current of a few milliamps tracks from one probe to the other and along the wires to the transistor **base** terminal. This small amount of current is able to open the transistor's **gate**, which allows a far greater current to flow from the **collector** terminal (c) to the emitter terminal (e). The circuit is then made.

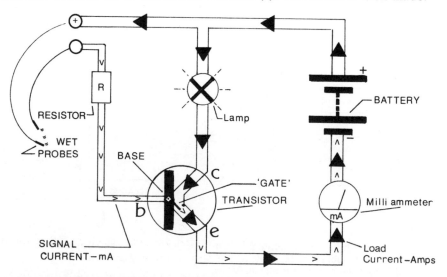

How a transistor works using a simple moisture detector circuit as an example.

It is wise to add a resistor in series formation with the base terminal (b). This will then provide a means of protection in case the probes touch each other.

Exercise 3.10   *Assembling an electronic circuit*

1. How can the copper backing strip serving a section of strip board be broken to isolate one component from the other? Answer in the space provided.

2. In your own words, describe why it is important not to bend a **component lead** too near the body of the component.

3. Describe the use of **tapered pins** in electronic assembly work.

4. For this practical exercise the following components will be needed:

   - A small section of strip board
   - One 60 milliamp (mA) bulb and holder
   - One 2N3053 or equivalent transistor
   - One 2.2 K resistor (i.e. 2.2 thousand ohms)
   - Two tapered terminal pins
   - One ORP12 light dependent resistor
   - Insulated tinned copper wire (size: 7/0.2)
   - One 9 volt battery
   - A soldering station and rosin-core solder

   With knowledge gained throughout this course, demonstrate to your **assessor** that you can assemble, test and commission a simple light-operated transistor switch. (See the figure on p. 193.) Note the following:

   1. Select the components required for this exercise according to the layout diagram. Check for correct type and values.
   2. All wires must be of a length appropriate to the requirements of the project.
   3. All component values must be visible and correctly mounted.
   4. Connecting wires should be routed as shown in the diagram.
   5. Components must be free from damage. Soldered joints must be free from solder splashes, spikes and pitting.
   6. Copper strips must be free from short circuits caused by solder splashes.
   7. A small gap should be seen between the wire insulation and the soldered joints.
   8. The circuit must be checked for faults and any faults corrected.
   9. The circuit must perform as intended.
   10. **Testing the circuit**:

       (a) First connect your 9 volt battery to the circuit. Take care that the **positive** (+) wire from the battery is connected to the positive terminal pin of the strip board. Similarly connect the black **negative** wire to the **negative** terminal pin.
       (b) Connecting the wrong way will damage the transistor.
       (c) Adjust the variable resistor so that the bulb light goes out in your present lighting conditions.
       (d) Cover up the light dependent resistor with a cloth or plastic aerosol cap and report to your assessor what happens.
       (e) Repeat the test under stronger lighting conditions such as under a strong fluorescent lamp or in the daylight near a window.

SI units used in electrical work

In 1960, the **General Conference of Weights and Measures** recommended a modern scientific system of weights and measures, which would be internationally recognised. In due course, the proposal was implemented and called **Système International d'Unités (International System of Units)**, commonly abbreviated as SI throughout the world. This replaced the now defunct **Metre, Kilogram, Second (MKS)** system, which was traditionally used before 1960.

SI units are divided into three categories:

1. Base unit
2. Derived units
3. Supplementary units

1. Base units

Unit	Symbol	Quantifier
amp	A	electric current
candela	cd	luminous intensity
kelvin	K	thermal temperature
kilogram	kg	mass
metre	m	length
mole	mol	amount of substance

SI units are always written in the singular form. For example, 1 mol and 100 mol, not 1 mol and 100 mols.

2. Derived units

Derived units are formed by combining two or more base units together. For example, the unit of electrical charge, the **coulomb** (symbol C), is the product of the base units **current** and **time**. Not all derived units are provided with individual terms of reference. Some, e.g. **magnetic field strength** (symbol A m^{-1}), are written combining both base units together, **amp per metre**.

There are many derived SI units that may be readily identified. The table below outlines a small selection of them.

Unit	Symbol	Quantifier
Celsius	°C	Temperature
farad	F	Capacitance
hertz	Hz	Frequency
henry	H	Inductance
joule	J	Energy
lumen	lm	Luminous flux
lux	lx	Illumination
newton	N	Force
ohm	Ω	Resistance
volt	V	Potential difference
watt	W	Power

3. Supplementary units

Just two units have been defined so far and both are dimensionless. The **steradian** (symbol **sr**) and the **radian** (symbol **rad**) are both supplementary units used for solid and plane angles respectively.

4. Multiplication factors and prefixes used in SI

Multiples and sub-multiples of units are offered in multiples of 10. The table below outlines the standard prefixes and multiplication factors used in association with SI units.

Prefix	Definition	Symbol	multiplication factor	Power
tera	One million million	T	1 000 000 000 000	10^{12}
giga	One thousand million	G	1 000 000 000	10^{9}
mega	One million	M	1 000 000	10^{6}
kilo	One thousand	k	1000	10^{3}
hecto	One hundred	h	100	10^{2}
deca	Ten	da	10	10^{1}
deci	One tenth	d	0.1	10^{-1}
centi	One hundredth	c	0.01	10^{-2}
milli	One thousandth	m	0.001	10^{-3}
micro	One millionth	µ	0.000 001	10^{-6}
nano	One thousand millionth	n	0.000 000 001	10^{-9}
pico	One million millionth	p	0.000 000 000 001	10^{-12}
femto	One thousand million millionth	f	0.000 000 000 000 001	10^{-15}
atto	One million million millionth	a	0.000 000 000 000 000 001	10^{-18}

Practical applications

1 TW (terawatts) of power, i.e. 1 000 000 000 000 watts.
2 GV (gigavolts) of potential difference, i.e. 2 000 000 000 volts.
3 MΩ (megohms) of resistance, i.e. 3 000 000 ohms.
4 kJ (kilojoules) of energy, i.e. 4000 joules.
5 cm (centimetres) of length, i.e. 0.05 metres.
6 mA (milliamps) of current, i.e. 0.006 amps.
7 µF (microfarads) of capacitance, i.e. 0.000 007 farads.
8 ps (picoseconds) of time, i.e. 0.000 000 000 008 seconds.

Recommended tool kit for electrical work

Choose your tools with care remembering that expensive tools can attract an opportunist thief. Never leave tools unattended and be wise when lending to site operatives. Try to insure against loss or theft but always read the conditions of insurance before committing yourself. Sometimes the listed exclusion clauses can be totally unsuitable.

Itemised alphabetically below are the basic requirements of an electrician's tool kit. Specialised tools, e.g. compression tools for copper terminations or hole saws and arbors, can be added as and when required.

Installation work

1. Adjustable conduit grips
2. Adjustable spanner (medium)
3. Bolster chisel
4. Bush spanner (20 mm)
5. Chalk line string
6. Cold chisel (200 mm)
7. Combination metric square
8. Electric multi-speed percussion drill (110 volts)
9. File handle(s)
10. Files (25 mm flat and 8 mm round)
11. Floorboard chisel
12. Junior hacksaw and blades
13. Hacksaw and spare blades
14. Hammer (claw type)
15. Hammer (lump)
16. High-speed twist drills (assorted)
17. Insulated wire cutters
18. Mallet (plastic or rubber)
19. Mole grips
20. Multimeter
21. Pad saw
22. Paint brush
23. Pencil
24. Philips screwdriver
25. Pliers (insulated)
26. Pliers (long-nosed and insulated)
27. Plumb bob and line
28. Rawlplug® jumper (manual hole maker)
29. Screwdriver (terminal type)
30. Screwdriver (100 mm)
31. Screwdriver (150 mm)
32. Screwdriver (300 mm)
33. Spanner set (metric open-ended)
34. Spanner set (metric box type)
35. Spanner set (small metric terminal type)
36. Spirit level (50 mm)

37. Spirit level (250 mm)
38. Suitable rule
39. Tap wrench (chuck type)
40. Tenon saw
41. Tool box (lockable)
42. Wood bits (10, 20, 25 and 32 mm)

Items such as stocks and dies, vices and heavy power-tools, etc., are usually supplied by the employer when electrical installation work is carried out.

Electronic work

1. Crimping tool
2. De-soldering tool
3. Desk lamp, miniature type
4. Diagonal cutters
5. Flush cutters
6. Insulated pliers
7. Jeweller's screwdriver set
8. Long-nose pliers
9. Multimeter
10. Neon test screwdriver
11. Pencils, soft grade
12. Pocket magnifying glass
13. Pocket pen torch
14. Small steel rule
15. Snipe-nose pliers
16. Soldering station
17. Spanner, small adjustable
18. Straight tweezers
19. Terminal screwdriver, screw gripping type
20. Trimtools, types 1, 2 and 3
21. Wire strippers, adjustable

Tools of a more specialised nature, such as anti-static devices, etc., are usually supplied by an employer when required.

Index